AN INTRODUCTION TO
RADIO W

Other Titles of Interest

BP89	Communication
BP91	An Introduction to Radio DXing
BP105	Aerial Projects
BP125	25 Simple Amateur Band Aerials
BP132	25 Simple SW Broadcast Band Aerials
BP136	25 Simple Indoor and Window Aerials
BP145	25 Simple Tropical and MW Band Aerials
BP176	A TV-DXers Handbook
BP195	An Introduction to Satellite Television
BP198	An Introduction to Antenna Theory
BP255	International Radio Stations Guide
BP257	An Introduction to Amateur Radio
BP275	Simple Short Wave Receiver Construction
BP276	Short Wave Superhet Receiver Construction
BP278	Experimental Antenna Topics
BP281	An Introduction to VHF/UHF for Radio Amateurs
BP289	Data and Formulae for Amateur Radio Enthusiasts
BP290	An Introduction to Amateur Communications Satellites

AN INTRODUCTION TO
RADIO WAVE PROPAGATION

by

J. G. Lee

BERNARD BABANI (publishing) LTD
THE GRAMPIANS
SHEPHERDS BUSH ROAD
LONDON W6 7NF
ENGLAND

Please Note

Although every care has been taken with the production of this book to ensure that any projects, designs, modifications and/or programs etc. contained herewith, operate in a correct and safe manner and also that any components specified are normally available in Great Britain, the Publishers do not accept responsibility in any way for the failure, including fault in design, of any project, design, modification or program to work correctly or to cause damage to any other equipment that it may be connected to or used in conjunction with, or in respect of any other damage or injury that may be so caused, nor do the Publishers accept responsibility in any way for the failure to obtain specified components.

Notice is also given that if equipment that is still under warranty is modified in any way or used or connected with home-built equipment then that warranty may be void.

First Published — February 1991

British Library Cataloguing in Publication Data
Lee, J. G.
  An introduction to radio wave propagation.
  1. Radio waves. Propagation
  I. Title
  621.38411

ISBN 0 85934 238 7

Printed and bound in Great Britain by Cox & Wyman Ltd, Reading

About the Author

James G. Lee holds a Bachelor of Arts Degree in Mathematics and Physics (Electronics) from the University of California at Los Angeles. While in military and government service he served as a Communications Specialist, and was involved in radio wave propagation prediction, signal planning, and major communication station system engineering in Germany and Greece during the Korean War.

He has held commercial Radiotelegraph and Radiotelephone licences, in addition to a radio amateur licence (W6VAT) continuously since 1944. He has written for several radio amateur journals in the United States since 1961. He has also been involved with ballistic missile, as well as satellite telemetry. Prior to retirement, he was a Satellite Ground Systems engineer, as well as a Systems Test Engineer.

Preface

One of the things most often taken for granted in the modern world is the ability to listen to and view programmes on radio or television. Just like turning on a lamp, a flick of the switch provides news, entertainment, sports, and yes, even educational programming. But the medium through which these programmes are provided to the public is hardly ever noticed unless something happens to cause it to fail. The ability to provide long distance communications to and from almost any spot on the surface of the Earth often depends on this "radio roof" called the ionosphere.

Although much has been discovered about radio wave propagation by way of the ionosphere, there is still much to be learned. The broad study of radio wave propagation encompasses the physics of the Sun, the solar wind, the Earth's magnetosphere, and even local weather conditions. Each new discovery leads to a better understanding of how this essentially indestructible resource can be used to further the communications needs of mankind.

This book has been written with the average electronics hobbyist in mind. Technical language and mathematics have been kept to a minimum in the effort to present a broad yet clear picture of the subject. The reader who is a radio amateur, as well as one who is a short-wave listener, will find explanations of propagation phenomena which both have experienced in their pursuit of communications enjoyment.

The story begins — as it should — with the Sun. The Sun is the most important physical entity in our world. The story describes in detail the effects this immensely powerful nuclear furnace has on our use and enjoyment of radio and television communications. Some small side trips have been made to illustrate some of the other effects of the Sun. The story does not really have an end, but only closing words which may be added to as new discoveries are made. For just as the Sun began it all, only the Sun can bring it to an end.

James G. Lee

Contents

	Page

Chapter 1
IT ALL STARTS WITH THE SUN 1
   Our Nuclear Furnace 2
   The Sun's Composition 3
   The Solar Wind 5
   Solar Emissions 7

Chapter 2
SUNSPOTS THEMSELVES 9
   The Structure of Sunspots 9
   Generators of Electrical Energy 11
   Sunspot Numbers 13
   The Maunder Minimum 15

Chapter 3
THE IONOSPHERE 19
   Through the Spheres to the Fringes 19
   The Troposphere 21
   The Stratosphere 21
   Discovery of the Fringes 22
   The Ionospheric Layers 23
   The D Layer 25
   The E Layer 27
   The Sporadic-E Layer 27
   The F Layer 27
   Ionospheric Variations 29
   Ionospheric Disturbances 32
   Sudden Ionospheric Disturbance (SID) 34
   Ionospheric Storms 34
   Polar Blackouts 35

Chapter 4
RADIO WAVE PROPAGATION 37
   Sky Wave Propagation 39
   Skip Distance 42
   Sky Wave Field Intensities 44
   Maximum Usable Frequency (MUF) 47

Page

Chapter 4 (Continued)
    Optimum Traffic Frequency (FOT) 50
    Lowest Usable Frequency (LUF) 50
    Multi-hop Propagation 53
    Trans-equatorial Propagation (TE) 57
    Grey Line Propagation 58
    Ground Wave Propagation 65
    Ground Wave Field Intensities 66
    Ground Wave Propagation Frequencies 67
    Tying Up Some Loose Ends 70

Chapter 5
  NON-IONOSPHERIC PROPAGATION 75
    Tropospheric Propagation 75
    Earth—Moon—Earth Propagation (EME) 78
    Path Losses, Power Budgets and Doppler Effects . . 79
    Power Budgets 81
    Artificial Satellite Communications 82
    Power Budgets Et Al 86
    Meteorite Propagation 87

Chapter 6
  NOISE 89
    Atmospheric Noise 89
    Man-made Noise 91
    Cosmic Noise 91
    Receiver Noise 95
    Some Final Thoughts 96

Appendix A
  LOGARITHMS AND DECIBELS 97
    Hearing and Sound Levels 98

Appendix B
  GLOSSARY 101

Index 111

Chapter 1

IT ALL STARTS WITH THE SUN

There are thousands of millions of galaxies in our Universe, and each galaxy contains thousands of millions of stars, some very similar to our own Sun. Yet our Sun is not a particularly noteworthy star. It is quite ordinary by interstellar standards. Although it appears to be a very stable star (it has been there some 15 thousand million years), in reality it was born, lives, and will die just like any other star in the Universe.

But despite its average status as a star, the Sun or its effects impact everything in our daily life. Its light and heat make all vegetation possible. Plants and animals need water, and here too the Sun is responsible for all of our rainfall.

It has been calculated that the average rainfall for the entire Earth is about 32 inches per annum. If all of it fell at one time, the entire globe would be flooded to a depth of nearly 1 metre. This amount of water weighs about 480 million million tons. Since water must be lifted by evaporation from every lake, river, and ocean to an altitude of about 1200 metres in order for it to fall as rain, this massive irrigation effort requires the expenditure of 220 thousand million horsepower continuously throughout the year.

This irrigation system has been at work for millions of years. Yet only a very small percentage of the Sun's energy which impacts the Earth is used to keep this rain-making effort in operation.

Every square metre of the Earth's surface which is fully exposed to the Sun receives about 1⅛ kilowatts continuously. Over a 12-hour period, this is about 48,600 kilowatt-hours. If we had to pay for this amount of energy, the size of our electric bill would soon bankrupt us. And this doesn't include any taxes our lawmakers might deem desirable.

Just these two simple examples provide an idea of the truly enormous amount of energy we receive from the Sun. But the Sun radiates energy in all directions, and the amount falling on, or near, the Earth is but a small fraction of the total amount radiated.

Since the average distance from the Earth to the Sun is just over 149.6 million kilometres (km), and the Sun's diameter is about 108 times that of the Earth, the amount of energy intercepted by the Earth is a mere one two-thousand millionth of the total energy radiated into space by the Sun.

Going back to the electric bill example, this means for every kilowatt the Earth receives, two-thousand million kilowatts are radiated out into interplanetary space. If the total amount of energy received by the Earth is multiplied by this factor, the Sun's output is about

340,000,000,000,000,000,000,000 kilowatts .

Not bad for an ordinary, inconspicuous star tucked away in a quite ordinary galaxy!

Our Nuclear Furnace

Scientists have long theorized as to the source of the Sun's energy. Scientists know the Sun is largely gaseous, and its gravitational forces are sufficiently strong to continuously attract its materials toward the centre, or core. Such contraction raises the temperature, and causes a tendency for the Sun to shrink. But in order for the Sun to maintain its output, scientists calculate it would have to shrink about 60 metres a year.

At this rate it could not have lasted for more than about ten million years and still maintain its output. So the "shrinking hypothesis" is invalid, and the other old hypothesis that meteors falling into the Sun help replenish its matter for conversion into energy also is not correct. It soon becomes obvious that the Sun's energy source is internal to the star itself.

Because of the Sun's appearance and heat output, it is tempting to think of the Sun as a furnace where ordinary combustion is taking place. Unfortunately, the Sun is too hot for such combustion. Burning, or oxidation, is a chemical process. The temperature of the Sun, with the exception of its sunspots, is far too hot to allow oxygen to combine chemically with any other element.

2

Sunspots, which will be discussed later, do have a somewhat lower temperature, and there is some indication that oxidation does take place within them. Because of the temperatures involved in the Sun, some other process has to provide the fuel for the immense radiation involved.

The development of what physicists call the "quantum theory" provided the answers. In 1926, Sir Arthur Eddington suggested that only sub-atomic nuclear processes could do the job. He calculated the temperature of the Sun core to be approximately 40 million degrees Celsius. At these temperatures, sub-atomic particles would have sufficient energy imparted to them to smash into one another and liberate large quantities of energy in doing so.

The problem other physicists found with this explanation was that like-particles repel one another, and would be less likely to fuse into a heavier element and release any energy. They believed that even at the elevated temperatures in the Sun's core, the repulsive forces would be too large to be overcome.

But in 1928, the new quantum theory showed that particles did not have to surmount the repulsion barrier, but could "tunnel" under it. Thus, Eddington's conjecture was plausible, and the nuclear "fusion" processes were workable. What was needed was a formula to show the actual mechanism.

In 1938, Hans Bethe and Carl von Weiszacker independently derived the mathematical equations which gave two possible nuclear reactions for the generation of solar energy. They showed the first possibility — the carbon cycle — changed hydrogen into helium, with carbon as a catalyst. This process liberates immense energy. The second process could change hydrogen into helium without using carbon, and was called the "proton-proton" chain. In the proton-proton chain, stable nitrogen atoms are struck with hydrogen nuclei (protons) and produce the necessary helium atoms and the release of large quantities of energy.

The Sun's Composition
Figure 1 shows a cross-section of the Sun's regions from the core outward. The central core is where the thermonuclear fusion originates. At a temperature of 14 million degrees

3

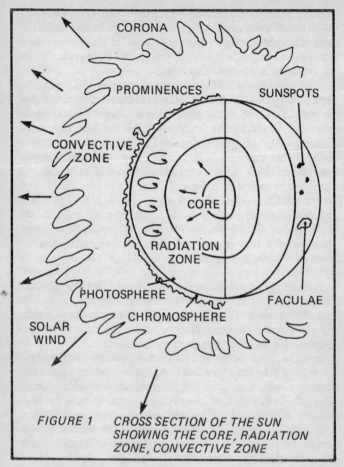

FIGURE 1   CROSS SECTION OF THE SUN
            SHOWING THE CORE, RADIATION
            ZONE, CONVECTIVE ZONE

Celsius, the core radiates heat out through the "radiation zone" for a distance of up to 470,000 km from the centre. Beyond this region, convection carries the heat a distance of about 225,000 km to the surface, or *photosphere*, which is only about 5000 km deep. The temperature of the photosphere ranges from 4500 to 5800 degrees Celsius.

Above the photosphere lies the *chromosphere* from 130,000 km out into the coronal area. Its temperature increases with its height above the photosphere to about 50,000 degrees Celsius. The pressure and density decrease rapidly with the height of the chromosphere as it merges into the *corona*.

The corona is a diffuse region and is invisible because of the intense light radiated by the Sun. It can be observed during an eclipse, or by making an artificial eclipse by placing an opaque disk over the image of the photosphere. The corona extends several million kilometres from the Sun and sends a stream of radiation, particulate matter, electrons, and protons out into the solar system at velocities ranging from 300 to 600 km per second.

The Solar Wind
The solar wind extends several million kilometres out into the solar system. For planets which have strong magnetic fields surrounding them, such as the Earth and Jupiter, it distorts the magnetic field as it sweeps around them.

Figure 2A shows the *plane of the ecliptic* which passes through the centres of the Sun and the Earth. In this instance, it is the winter solstice in the northern hemisphere, since the North Pole is pointing away from the Sun at an angle of about 23 degrees from true vertical.

Figure 2B shows the basic effect of the solar wind as it impinges on the Earth's magnetic field, or *magnetosphere*. The solar wind sweeps around the magnetosphere since it is not strong enough to do much more than distort it. Some energetic particles do penetrate the magnetosphere to varying depths and result in the trapped-radiation belts around our planet. The belts are known as the Van Allen belts after the American physicist, Dr James Van Allen, who discovered them.

The force of the solar wind varies in magnitude due not only to changes in the emission rates of the particulate matter, but also to the fact that the Sun is a rotating body. This imparts a spiralling motion to the released particles. Measurements of the Sun's motion show that its equator has a rotational rate of about 27 days.

The Sun is a gaseous body, and does not rotate as a solid body such as the Earth does. This rotational rate at the Sun's

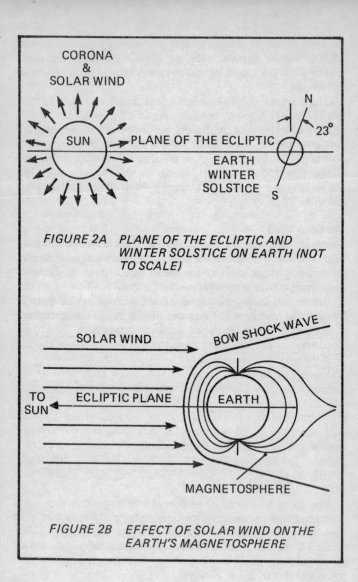

CORONA
&
SOLAR WIND

SUN PLANE OF THE ECLIPTIC

N

23°

EARTH
WINTER
SOLSTICE

S

FIGURE 2A   PLANE OF THE ECLIPTIC AND
WINTER SOLSTICE ON EARTH (NOT
TO SCALE)

SOLAR WIND

BOW SHOCK WAVE

TO
SUN

ECLIPTIC PLANE

EARTH

MAGNETOSPHERE

FIGURE 2B   EFFECT OF SOLAR WIND ON THE
EARTH'S MAGNETOSPHERE

poles takes about 35 days for one complete revolution. It is this difference in rotational rate for a solar "day" that gives rise to such features as sunspots, flares, and other prominences visible on the Sun's surface.

Solar Emissions

We see the light emitted by the Sun, but we can only feel the heat it radiates. This means there is not only visible radiation from the Sun, but "dark" or invisible radiation as well. One of these dark emissions — ultraviolet radiation — provides the Earth with some subtle benefits. Although too much exposure to it can be quite dangerous.

Light is an electromagnetic entity, but heat from the Sun would not seem to qualify as that type of radiation. Yet it is. Everyone is familar with rainbows which are often seen following rainstorms. The colours range from red to violet at opposite edges of the rainbow. These visible light waves have wavelengths which vary from about 0.7 millionths of a metre (μm) for red light, to about 0.4 μm for violet light. Figure 3 shows the visible light region and the surrounding region.

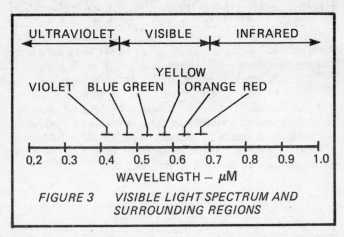

FIGURE 3   VISIBLE LIGHT SPECTRUM AND SURROUNDING REGIONS

Thus our eyes are sensitive to a rather narrow range of frequencies from about 400 million million hertz (Hz) at the red end of the spectrum, to about 800 million million Hz at the violet end. But our skin picks up where our eyes leave off.

In the region "below" visible red — the *infra-red* region — the slower frequencies manifest themselves as heat. The region "above" the violet — the *ultraviolet* — is also detected by our skin, and causes "tanning" and sunburn. Excessive exposure to the infra-red as well as the ultraviolet can be quite dangerous. The response of the skin to these dark emissions is much slower than the response of the eye to visible light.

Certain other emissions of the Sun are important as well. Particulate matter, in the form of electrons, protons, and neutrons are also carried out into interstellar space. Since these particles have mass, their velocities are much lower than the visible photons which travel at the speed of light. Their impact is felt by their interaction with the magnetosphere producing propagation blackouts, and the auroral displays seen at the North and South magnetic poles.

The study of these emissions, along with some early radar investigations under the auspices of the National Research Council of Canada, have shown additional solar electromagnetic effects (other than sunspots) on radio wave propagation. Although sunspots have been observed for centuries, modern measuring techniques and equipment have provided a clearer picture of all of the elements which affect propagation.

For many years, however, the "dark spots" appearing on the Sun's surface were believed to be the primary cause of not only our ability to communicate over long distances by radio, but to also affect other more mundane subjects, such as weather, tree growth, temperature, and other biological effects. They are a major contributor in one or more of these areas, and so deserve a closer look.

Chapter 2

SUNSPOTS THEMSELVES

Although the annals of some very early Chinese dynasties discuss the observation of disturbances, or blemishes, on the Sun, it wasn't until Galileo turned the first telescope towards the Sun in the early 17th century that these drifting disturbances called *sunspots* were studied in earnest. Some astronomers of those days thought they were merely dirt specks on the lenses of the telescopes, but their consistent appearances over the years soon convinced even the most sceptical that they truly were a phenomenon occurring on the Sun.

Galileo noticed that they drifted across the face of the Sun at about the Sun's rotational rate. He developed a projection method for indirectly observing the Sun and its surface to prevent serious eye injury to the observer. His method projected the view through the eyepiece onto a white background so the observer had an indirect view of the Sun. He then made drawings of the spots, which showed their variable nature as well as their movements across the visible solar disk.

As with many contemporaries of his day, his excellent discoveries and efforts were met with condemnation by the religious authorities. As with all such negativism, it prevented any real progress and held back other discoveries about the Sun for decades. Nevertheless, discreet investigations did continue, and provided the start of solar observations and records which continue today. But first, what are sunspots and how do they come about?

The Structure of Sunspots

In order to understand the structure of sunspots, some investigation into their origin is necessary. In spite of centuries of observation, the "how" of their existence is still subject to debate. That they appear to be disturbances much like terrestrial hurricanes or typhoons is not in question. What is in question is their appearance at particular latitudes, their progress towards the solar equator as the cycle progresses, and their reversal of magnetic poles in alternate cycles.

An early hypothesis stated the appearance of sunspots was due to disturbances by planets in the solar system. Systematic observations however failed to show a correlation of planetary cycles with sunspot cycles. Scientific consensus today among astronomers has it that the causes lie completely within the Sun itself.

One early sunspot theory considered the Sun's "atmospheric" circulation to be similar to the Earth's. There is a convection flow of tides and winds on the Earth, and if the Sun's gaseous matter near the surface acted in a similar manner, then parallels might be drawn to explain the sunspots' formation and movements.

The "hurricane" hypothesis falls apart however due to some distinct differences in the fluid flow and temperature differences between the two bodies. In the case of the Earth, hurricanes originate between about 8 degrees and 15 degrees latitude above and below the equator. Sunspots originate at about 35 degrees to 40 degrees above and below the solar equator.

Terrestrial hurricanes move first in a westerly direction. In the northern hemisphere they often swing back to the north, and on some occasions, swing back to the east before striking land and dissipating. Sunspots move toward the solar equator in a westerly direction only. They sometimes make more than one traverse around the Sun's surface before they dissipate.

Temperature plays a large part in the formation of terrestrial hurricanes. The South Atlantic Ocean rarely sees hurricanes, since its surface temperature is low at the latitudes where hurricanes originate. The temperature differential between the Sun's layers and the Earth's atmosphere and oceans is immense. Hurricanes often dissipate over water without striking land, and this is due to a cooling of the sea as the hurricane moves north.

But although there is still no universally accepted theory of how sunspots originate, their structure has been studied extensively beginning in 1908 by the American scientist Dr George Ellery Hale at the Mount Wilson Observatory in California. Hale invented the "spectroheliograph" by which he could photograph the spectral lines of incandescent hydrogen and calcium which make up a large part of the Sun's surface.

His apparatus was a photographic film plate which moved across the image of the Sun formed by a telescope. A specially arranged slit filtered out all light except the one emitted by the desired chemical element. His spectacular photographs showed great clouds of hydrogen gas and calcium vapour swirling in the neighbourhood of sunspots as though they were in the grip of a gigantic whirlpool.

Hale was able to photograph the whirlpool – or vortex – at different depths and get a cross-section of the sunspot which extended well down below the Sun's surface. The photographs also showed that spots north of the solar equator rotated in the opposite direction from those south of the solar equator. This is very similar to tropical hurricanes here on Earth.

But unlike hurricanes, sunspots often appear in groups. Their size can vary from just a few hundred miles across to groups encompassing areas over 400,000 square km of the Sun's surface. Some individual spots are capable of containing several planets as large as the Earth with space left over. One of the largest sunspots ever photographed was over 145,000 km in diameter, and its associated smaller spots covered an area of about 30 times the Earth's surface.

Such large groups can have lifetimes up to several solar months. Smaller sunspots often last only a few days by contrast. Others will drift across the face of the Sun and disappear behind the Sun, never to be seen again. But whatever their size, we on Earth feel their effects.

Generators of Electrical Energy

At about the same time Hale was using his spectroheliograph to photograph the Sun, other Mount Wilson observers made a crucial discovery. It has long been known that light waves are distorted when a powerful magnetic field occurs near the light source. Examination of the light coming from the centre of the sunspots was found to be distorted in exactly the same way that light waves can be distorted in the laboratory with a powerful magnet.

Although sunspots appear very dark on the surface of the Sun, it is only because the surrounding light from the Sun is very much brighter than the light sunspots themselves emit.

11

The distortion of their light showed that the sunspots were not only immense vortexes of whirling gases, but also were the centres of powerful magnetic fields. This crucial discovery supported a theory concerning changes in the Earth's magnetic field and sunspots.

Students of elementary electricity know that an electrical current passing through a circular wire loop induces a magnetic field within the loop. Inserting an iron bar into the plane of the loop, and perpendicular to it, causes a definite increase in the strength of the magnetic field.

The source of the Earth's magnetic field has also been one of conjecture as well. The discovery of the "lodestone" by early navigators of the sea showed slight changes in the direction of these crude compasses not only as the seasons changed, but daily — or *diurnal* — variations as well.

It appears that there are two possible sources for the Earth's magnetic field. Presumably, there is a very large core of nickel-iron at the Earth's centre which acts as a bar-magnet having a relatively permanent "set" like the lodestone. If this core is molten, as may be the case, then its residual magnetism may not be sufficient to provide the total magnetic strength we measure at the Earth's surface. The reason for this is that heating a magnet often destroys its magnetism.

The second source is similar to the loop of wire which has electric current flowing through it. The flow of electricity is commonly believed to be due to the motion of electrons. But an electron is a *"charged particle"*, and charged particles are called *"ions"*. Any of these ions which strike the Earth's magnetic field will be deflected around the Earth. There they will form a "circulating" or *"ring"* current just like the current flow in the circular loop of wire above.

The ring current around the Earth will have an associated magnetic field, and with the nickel-iron core of the Earth acting in concert with the magnetic field generated by the ring current, the magnetic field of the Earth will be strengthened. Thus, any and all ions which the solar wind brings to the Earth will affect this combined magnetic field. Any variation in the emissions of the sunspots directed by the solar wind to the Earth will cause similar variations in the magnetic field of the Earth.

To be sure, there are other contributors such as solar flares, cosmic rays, and meteorites which cause localized variations. But by and large, it is the ionic density in the far, upper reaches of the Earth's atmosphere that cause the fluctuations seen in the delicate needles of "magnetometers" set up to measure the Earth's magnetic fields.

Thus sunspots are definitely electrical generators. Every electric field has an associated magnetic field, and the large sunspots have magnetic fields thousands of times stronger than that of the Earth. By comparing the distortion of hydrogen light produced by a magnetic field in the laboratory with the measured distortion in sunspots, the strength of the fields associated with them can be easily calculated. But a new discovery was made when the result of two consecutive sunspot seasons were compared.

Just as there is a dual polarity of "positive" and "negative" associated with electricity, there are two types of magnetic polarity as well. The type which attracts the north-pointing end of a compass needle is called "negative", and its complement which attracts the south-pointing needle is called "positive".

The astronomers at Mount Wilson found that the sunspots from a new cycle of activity had opposite *magnetic polarity* from those of the previous cycle. There was a reversal of polarity as an old cycle passed into a new one. Heretofore, the usual cycle of sunspots had been considered to be an average of 11 years. But these new developments suggest that the actual cycle period should be 23 years. In actuality, the 11-year average is just that — an average. Sunspot cycles have been as short as 8 years, and as long as 18 years, but the polarity reversal at the start of a new cycle has remained constant.

Sunspot Numbers

Many European astronomers began keeping detailed sunspot records in the middle of the 18th century. But as often happens, it was not a scientist but a hobbyist, who determined the fact that sunspots varied at a cyclical rate. Hendrick Schwabe, in reality a pharmacist from Dessau, Germany, is given the credit for the discovery of the sunspot cycle.

13

Beginning in the early 19th century, he kept very detailed notes of the sunspots he observed day in and day out, year after year, through his telescope. His determination, as well as his intellectual curiosity, showed him a distinct pattern was beginning to emerge after a few years of observation.

He noticed some years passed with only a few sunspots showing on the Sun's surface. Following these years he noticed the number increasing to literally hundreds of sunspots. After more than 20 years of daily observations, Schwabe published a paper in 1843 on his findings. He suggested in his paper that the cycle length from minimum to maximum and back to minimum was approximately a decade.

Shortly after Schwabe's paper, the Zurich Solar Observatory in Switzerland which had been collecting daily counts from numerous sources, published an "index of solar activity" related to the counts. It was called the "Zurich number", and was devised by the then-director, Rudolph Wolf. This was the first attempt to standardize the reporting from other sources.

Different observers, and observatories, had different types and sizes of telescopes. Some observers had more visual acuity than others, and there is nothing more useless than non-standardized data in science. Wolf realised this and also realised that a large sunspot had a greater impact than a smaller one. In addition, he realised that a group of sunspots, while not necessarily equal to a large one of similar area, was more significant than just one sunspot alone.

He devised a mathematical equation which took into account the number of individual sunspots, groups of sunspots, and an arbitrary factor which took into account the type and optical power of the telescope used, the viewing conditions, and the individual observer. The equation is:

$$R = k(10g + f),$$

where

  R = Wolf's relative sunspot number
  f = total number of sunspots
  g = observed number of sunspot groups, and

k = an arbitrary factor for standardizing the observations.

The factor "k" varies around unity, or 1.0. Observers who used small telescopes would use a factor slightly above 1.0 since it was deemed more difficult to count small sunspots with such equipment. For large observatories such as Mount Wilson, the k-factor was a little less than 1.0 because "seeing" the sunspots would be more easily done. Although the k-factor might seem a little too arbitrary, in practice it has proved to be quite good.

The factor of "10" which multiplies "g" was selected by Wolf to give groups of sunspots greater emphasis. Although the result of the equation is to produce a *sunspot number*, it really produces a measure of solar "*activity*".

There is one other method which has been used to plot solar activity. It is based on the spotted "area" on the surface of the Sun, and then comparing it with the total surface area of the Sun. The Royal Observatory at Greenwich records these values, and in the United States they are published by the Department of Commerce Weather Review. But by far, the Zurich, or Wolf numbers are most often used for radio wave propagation calculations.

The Maunder Minimum

Scientists have long believed that sunspots have a profound effect on the Earth's weather. If, however, you ask a meteorologist he will most likely say he has enough to handle with temperatures, pressures, humidity, zonal indices, and analysis of the air masses than to worry about one more variable when it comes to predicting the weather.

Any meteorologist will agree that it is the Sun's heat which causes our weather patterns, and without it there would be precious little weather to predict. He might even point out that much of our seasonal changes, lengths of days, and the amount of heat we receive are also affected by our planetary position with respect to the Sun. At the winter solstice, for example, the Earth is at "*perihelion*" or its point of closest approach to the Sun. Due to the tilt of the Earth's axis, the northern hemisphere receives less heating than during the spring, summer, or autumn and so our weather is much colder. But, he will conclude, this is "climatology" and not meteorology we are discussing.

Any examination of climatological data will show, however, definite long term effects such as drought, and excessive rainfall in various regions. Our meteorologist is quite correct, since any studies of these phenomena are not rightfully the domain of day-to-day forecasting. Fortunately there has been extensive investigation into certain archaeological areas which show specific correlation to sunspot activity over several millennia.

Some years ago, Professor A. E. Douglass, of the University of Arizona, began investigating tree-ring growth. Both an astronomer and an archaeologist, Douglass was the director of Steward Observatory, at Tucson, and founded the Tree Ring Laboratory there.

He had always been interested in the growth of vegetation as an index of climatology and as a history of sunspots. In examining the trunks of fallen trees, he had noted periods of rapid growth often alternated with periods of slow, or retarded growth. By counting these periods he noted that many specimens showed ten to twelve rings separating the two periods of growth. It suggested to Douglass there might be a verifiable correlation between tree-ring growth and the sunspot cycle.

He developed an optical measuring device to aid in analysing the tens of thousands of tree-rings which underwent his scrutiny. It was not long before he was able to clearly distinguish intervals of seven, eleven, and twenty-three years to which his tree specimens had definitely responded.

Because climatological differences do exist, his examination of trees in the southwestern area of the United States showed other phenomena as well. He was able to correlate droughts which had occurred, as well as evidence of vast forest fires which had occurred in primeval forests. He was able to separate and recognise these archaeological "footprints" and make allowances for these catastrophic happenings.

Over the course of his investigations he documented tree-ring records back nineteen hundred years for trees in the southwestern United States using petrified logs as well as recent growth trees. He also investigated the giant Sequoias in the northwestern United States and here his records were correlated back in time three thousand, two hundred years.

At times, there were gaps in these periods. Here, Douglass the archaeologist prevailed. He knew there were many ruins of ancient Hopi Indian villages in the southwestern United States. He knew there would be specimens and fragments of pottery used by these ancient Indians. By learning the chronology of these fragments, he believed he could find and unearth ancient timbers in these old villages for the periods he was interested in.

His belief was correct, and in all but one incident, he was able to locate old timbers whose tree-ring patterns allowed him to fill in his chronology almost completely. He had uncovered one nagging doubt, however, as to the veracity of his whole theory. Try as he might, he was unable to confirm an indication that between the years 1645 to 1715 there had been a dearth of sunspots. There was supposed to have been a sunspot maximum occurring during that time, based on the eleven-year cycle. Yet he found just the opposite.

Quite to his surprise one morning in 1922, he received a letter from Professor E. W. Maunder of the Royal Observatory in Greenwich which gave him the missing evidence. Professor Maunder had been aware of Douglass' work, and quite innocently wished to convey to him some very interesting sunspot data he had recently uncovered.

Maunder's investigations of sunspot records had turned up undeniable evidence that there had in fact been a great dearth of sunspots during the period from 1645 to 1715. Maunder said that if there was a real connection between sunspots and Douglass' examination of tree-ring growth, his tree-ring data should show this period to be lacking in sunspots. This single letter prevented Douglass' discarding years of intensive study and field work.

This very long period of no appreciable sunspot activity has become known as the Maunder Minimum. The implications of the Maunder Minimum are that our Sun is truly a living, changing star, and that we may expect the unexpected from it. While our records go back a few thousand years, the Sun is just approaching middle age at about 15 thousand million years.

The introduction of Carbon-14 dating methods have further confirmed not only the Maunder Minimum, but solar activity anomalies from tree-rings. When carbon-dioxide is assimilated into living things — trees in this example — the radioactive isotopes begin to disintegrate at known rates.

By comparing the amount of Carbon-14 remaining and comparing it with a presumed original amount in the tree, it is possible to date the time the fossil tree existed. Because the Carbon-14 formation is related to solar activity as well as cosmic rays, it can track periods of solar activity. A quiet Sun causes an increase in Carbon-14 content, and an active Sun reduces its amounts.

As little as a ten percent change in Carbon-14 amounts is considered significant, and Carbon-14 was found to increase by 20% during the period of the Maunder Minimum. Another minimum lasting 90 years between 1460 and 1550 has been identified, as well as a prolonged period of high solar activity during the late 12th and early 13th centuries. In view of this data, the 21st century might bring some very interesting surprises.

Chapter 3

THE IONOSPHERE

The intense bombardment of radiation and particulate matter carried to Earth by the solar wind affects our atmosphere, beginning with its thin outer fringes at an altitude of 500 km, down to 60 km above the surface of the Earth. While the weaker components of radiation are swept aside by the magnetosphere, some radiation and particulate matter have sufficient strength to penetrate well into the atmosphere.

Through the Spheres to the Fringes

The Greek word *atmos* means "vapour", and while our atmosphere does contain water vapour in varying amounts, we normally think of the atmosphere as being a dry gas. It is composed mainly of nitrogen (78%) and oxygen (21%), but it is not a homogeneous mass throughout its entirety.

Although our meteorological elements such as pressure, humidity, and temperature vary from place to place, and with time, the vertical variations are significantly less than the horizontal ones. It is therefore possible to draw a *standard atmosphere* showing the essential features of the vertical structure. Figure 4 shows an idealised picture of the atmosphere's structure.

The average atmospheric conditions below 25 km have been well explored by aircraft, and balloons, equipped with instruments. Above this altitude, there has been somewhat less exploration, but the bulk of the studies have included the effects of radio waves, aurora borealis, and meteors. As a result it is possible to outline the general structure at least up to about 160 km above sea-level.

The decrease in pressure follows closely the decrease in air density as altitude increases. At about 50 km above sea-level the pressure is about 1/1000 of the sea-level value of 760 millimetres (mm) of mercury. At 100 km it has dropped still further to about 1/1,000,000 of the sea-level value.

Putting it another way, at sea-level the *mean free path* between air molecules is approximately 1/84,000 of a mm. At

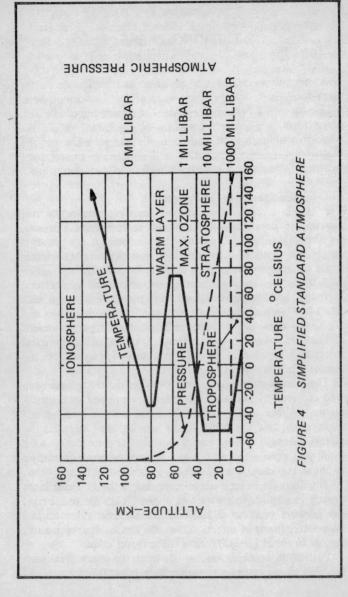

ATMOSPHERIC PRESSURE

0 MILLIBAR

1 MILLIBAR

10 MILLIBAR

1000 MILLIBAR

IONOSPHERE

TEMPERATURE

WARM LAYER

MAX. OZONE

STRATOSPHERE

PRESSURE

TROPOSPHERE

ALTITUDE—KM

TEMPERATURE °CELSIUS   FIGURE 4   SIMPLIFIED STANDARD ATMOSPHERE

20

100 km it is just over 25.4 mm, and at 250 km the mean free path between air molecules is about 25 metres. This great distance between molecules at the fringes of the atmosphere reduces their recombination rate when they have been ionized by ultraviolet radiation.

The Troposphere

The lowest layer of our atmosphere — the troposphere — contains 75% of the mass of the atmosphere, and 100% of all the moisture and dust. It extends up to about 11 km on the average. The Earth is not a perfect sphere, but has a sizeable equatorial bulge. As a result, the upper limit of the troposphere — the tropopause — can vary from about 8 km at the poles to around 16 km at the Equator.

In addition, the height of the tropopause varies with temperature. One of the most striking features of the troposphere is its abrupt change in temperature after a steady decline with altitude. An abrupt change in temperature brings with it an abrupt change in air density. This means a change in the dielectric constant of the air mass which can affect radio wave propagation at television frequencies for example.

In addition, the troposphere has the most "overturning" of air in the atmosphere. This overturning can vary from small localized areas of turbulence, known as "air pockets" to aircraft passengers, up to large weather systems such as hurricanes, typhoons, and large thunderstorms. Heavy rainfall and temperature *inversions* can also change the local dielectric constant of the air mass and affect television reception as well. Tropospheric propagation will be covered in more detail later.

The Stratosphere

If the troposphere has relatively frequent air mass overturnings, then the stratosphere is that area above the troposphere which is normally quite stable from day to day. From the figure it can be seen that its temperature is stable, and it has essentially no moisture or dust content. Occasionally volcanic eruptions change this situation, but the stratosphere contains another very vital element to life on Earth.

That vital element is *ozone*, the point at which radiation from the Sun penetrates its deepest into our atmosphere. The

21

levels of ozone vary over the seasons, and there is no sharp dividing line between the upper stratosphere and the warm layers above it which contain ozone as well. Sometimes called the *mesosphere* or the *chemosphere*, the warm zone temperature is seen to increase again with altitude.

In the warm area above the stratosphere, the temperatures reach a maximum of about 80 degrees Celsius which is considerably warmer than the Sahara reaches under its hottest conditions. It is generally agreed by scientists studying this area that it is due to selective absorption of ultraviolet radiation. While the greatest concentration of ozone lies between 25 and 30 km altitude, the rate of production and destruction of ozone is highest in the layer above 30 km.

Discovery of the Fringes

The idea of communications by wireless waves is generally attributed to the Italian scientist, Guglielmo Marconi. In the late 1890's Marconi successfully transmitted signals across the English Channel. He chose a formidable challenge for his next experiment in wireless signalling — bridging the Atlantic Ocean.

In late 1901, near the town of Poldhu, in Cornwall, he erected a large "spark" transmitter, and a sizeable transmitting aerial he had designed. He and two of his assistants then sailed to a location now known as Signal Hill, near the town of St. Johns, Newfoundland. Here he set up his receiving location.

In the afternoon of December 12, 1901, and using a kite-borne aerial, he heard three faint "clicks" in his earphones. It was the Morse letter "S", his pre-arranged signal, being transmitted from Poldhu some 3200 km away. The Atlantic Ocean had been successfully crossed by wireless signals.

Marconi was not sure just exactly how it had occurred but it had. About one year later, two scientists, Arthur Kennelly in the United States, and Oliver Heaviside in Great Britain, each published papers suggesting there was an electrified region high up in the Earth's atmosphere. Using the German physicist Heinrich Hertz's observation that although wireless waves travelled in straight lines, they could be deflected by electrically conducting obstacles in their path, Kennelly and

Heaviside proposed that it was this electrified layer which reflected Marconi's signal back to Earth across the Atlantic.

The region became known as the Kennelly-Heaviside layer, and it was to take two decades before its existence was verified. Today we know it as the "E" layer, and its existence was verified in 1924 by another British scientist, Edward V. Appleton. He and his co-workers had measured the angle of arrival of the signals from a nearby transmitter. The angle of arrival was such that the signals could only have come from a reflecting layer in the Earth's atmosphere approximately 160 km high. For his pioneering work in the field of radio wave propagation, Appleton was knighted.

The following year, two American scientists, G. Breit and M. A. Tuve demonstrated the ability to accurately measure the heights of the Kennelly-Heaviside and Appleton layers as they became known. Breit and Tuve used a form of primitive radar to send short pulses vertically, and then measure the presence of an echo which had been returned to Earth by the layers. By knowing that radio waves travel with the speed of light, they were able to deduce the layer heights quite accurately.

Later experiments, using pulses on different frequencies, showed a *critical frequency* existed above which the pulse would no longer be returned to Earth. Other experiments at various locations around the world showed the critical frequency varied hourly, seasonally, and geographically. This proved the layers were heavily influenced by the Sun. In 1927 measurements were made during an eclipse of the Sun which showed a sharp decrease in the critical frequency as the eclipse progressed. Figure 5 is a typical curve of the degree of ionization during a solar eclipse.

From these historic experiments it was concluded that the primary solar radiation causing these layers was ultraviolet emission. The low pressures and the variable densities which exist at these extreme atmospheric heights allow the ultraviolet radiation to generate high concentrations of free electrons. The aggregation of these layers has become known as the *ionosphere*.

The Ionospheric Layers

When an atom is in a neutral state, with its electrons orbiting

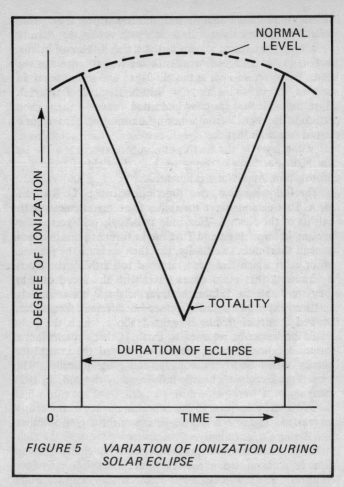

FIGURE 5   VARIATION OF IONIZATION DURING
            SOLAR ECLIPSE

quietly about the nucleus, it neither radiates nor absorbs energy. But when sufficient energy is applied to the atom, either in the form of heat or other electromagnetic radiation, the electrons can be knocked loose and the atom becomes ionized. If the applied energy continues in sufficient strength the atom will not recombine, but will stay in its ionized state.

The ultraviolet radiation causing this ionizing effect loses energy. Consequently it will reach a point where its intensity is no longer sufficient to disrupt the stable, neutral atoms. Because of the changes in the Sun's angle with respect to the Earth, there is a seasonal variation of the received radiation. In addition, diurnal — or daily — variations also occur which affect the overall amount of ionization present at any given period of the year. Figure 6 shows the various layers and their relationship to the Earth.

The D Layer

Sir Robert Watson-Watt, the developer of radar and an early associate of Appleton, gave the name "ionosphere" to the electrified region in the upper atmosphere, but it was Appleton who named the initial group of layers. He named the Kennelly-Heaviside layer the "E" layer after the symbol normally used as an "electric vector".

Appleton also discovered a layer above the E layer which he named the F layer. Then, following his discovery of a layer just below the E layer, he called it the D layer. He said that this system left letters above and below for other layers, if and when they should be discovered.

The D layer exists at an altitude of 50 to 90 km. It is the lowest region with stable pronounced degrees of ionization. Because it takes much more energy to ionize the atmosphere at this low altitude, the D layer only exists during the daylight hours.

Its ionization level is the lowest of all the layers as a result and reaches its peak ionization level at noon, and then vanishes after sunset. It is primarily an absorptive layer due to the high rate of recombination of its ionized particles. Partly because of the high absorption, the D layer does not show up well on ionospheric sounding equipment. Not much is known about the layer, but frequencies below 300 kilohertz (kHz) may be reflected from it.

It is mainly apparent to the listener through its nightly disappearance when distant broadcast stations become audible. These distant stations then vanish at sunrise when the D layer begins reappearing. When solar flares or other ionospheric disturbances appear, the D layer assumes a major role in the

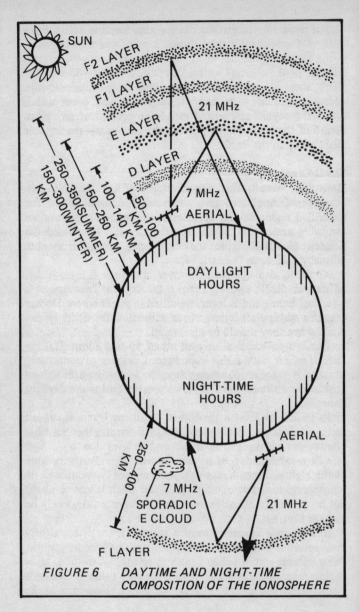

FIGURE 6   DAYTIME AND NIGHT-TIME
           COMPOSITION OF THE IONOSPHERE

absorption of radio waves. It severely limits the penetration of radio waves to the higher layers during these times.

The E Layer

This layer is a distinct layer above the D layer although their boundaries blend together. The degree of ionization of the E layer is greater than that of the D layer and, in general, follows the Sun's position in the sky closely. It occupies the region of 90 to 125 km above the surface of the Earth.

The E layer is a stable layer, but its maximum ionization is greatest at noon. It appears in all seasons, although its height may vary from the Sun's position in the sky. At night it too disappears, and although it is readily seen on ionospheric sounding equipment, it provides additional absorption as well as being a reflector of lower frequency radio waves. It is also associated with a little understood phenomenon called the *"sporadic-E"* layer.

The Sporadic-E Layer

As the name implies, sporadic-E activity consists of ionized regions which come and go in an irregular fashion. They most often appear at an altitude of 100 km, and are therefore associated with the E layer. Little is known about the cause of the sporadic-E effect.

These regions occur most often during the daylight hours in the summer, but have been seen at night and during the wintertime. They are very thin layers, often no more than a kilometre in depth, and may be only 70 to 150 square km in area. These ionized "clouds" often last for several hours before dissipating.

They often drift with velocities of several hundred kilometres an hour, and normally in a westerly direction in the northern hemisphere. What produces them is still somewhat of a mystery. Wind shears in the upper atmosphere are thought to be contributors to their formation, and they also have been noted during auroral displays.

The F Layer

The F layer is not only the most volatile of layers, it is also the most important ionized region for long distance communication.

The F layer extends above the E layer several hundred kilometres, particularly in the summer time. It is the region of highest ionization, and therefore some ionization is present at all hours.

During daylight hours, the degree of ionization and the volatility of the F layer is such that it often becomes two distinct layers — the F1 and the F2 layers. The F1 layer extends from just above the E layer at about 90 km up to 250 km. It is relatively stable at these altitudes, and like the lower D and E layers disappears at night. The F1 layer critical frequency follows the Sun angle closely, and is a maximum at noon time.

The F2 layer is the highest of the two layers and varies in altitude both seasonally and diurnally. During winter in the northern hemisphere, it extends up to 350 km. During the summer time it has reached heights of 500 km. During night-time hours, the F1 layer essentially disappears, and the F2 layer becomes the predominant F layer but at a height somewhere between that of the F1 layer and its daytime height. It occupies a region at night between 250 and 420 km.

Because it is the uppermost layer, it receives the greatest radiation flux and is therefore subject to greater variation not only diurnally, but hourly as well. The rise in ionization at sunrise is very rapid, but there is a time lag between maximum radiation and maximum ionization. Maximum ionization usually peaks in the afternoon before decreasing in the evening.

The F2 layer also appears to be greatly affected by solar heat since the height of ionization is much higher in the summer than in winter. Since heat causes a gas to expand, ionization can occur when regions of lower density appear. The ion density of the F2 layer is greater during daylight in winter, even though energy from the Sun is less in the northern hemisphere than in summer. As the atmosphere contracts toward nightfall, the two individual layers combine at a lower altitude, but in doing so keep the ionization intensity higher than might be expected during this time of day.

Ionospheric Variations

All of the effects which have been discussed in earlier sections are dependent upon the variations in ultraviolet radiation which strike the ionosphere. Most of these variations are cyclical in nature. The main variations which fit this group are:

1. Daily or diurnal
2. Geographical
3. Seasonal, and
4. Multi-year variations.

Diurnal variations are of course due to the Earth's rotation about its own axis. These variations can be easily plotted as shown in Figure 7 for a spring (or autumn) day. During these times the amount of sunshine is about twelve hours per day. Only the E, F1, and F2 layers are shown in the figure.

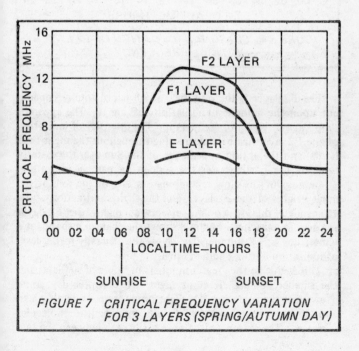

FIGURE 7   CRITICAL FREQUENCY VARIATION
FOR 3 LAYERS (SPRING/AUTUMN DAY)

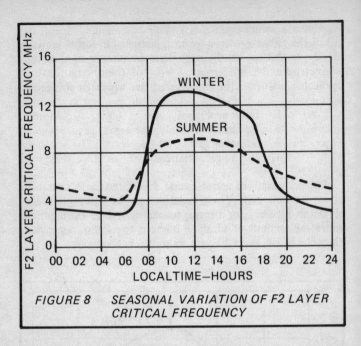

FIGURE 8   SEASONAL VARIATION OF F2 LAYER
            CRITICAL FREQUENCY

The F2 layer is the only one which is not totally dependent upon the amount of radiation striking it. The apparent
"dip" at sunrise is not really a dip. The intensity of ionization
of the F2 layer has been decreasing throughout the night-time
hours, and the abrupt appearance of the Sun over the easterly
limb of the Earth causes the sudden increase in ionization.

Because of the slow recombination rate of the ions at the
great heights of the F2 layer, and the slight contraction of the
atmosphere due to cooling effects at night, the F2 layer
remains in existence. Figure 8 shows the change in shape for a
winter day and a summer day. Note the generally higher level
of ionization during a summer night.

This is due to the greater numbers of hours of sunlight, and
the smaller cooling effect at night. The winter day graph
shows just the opposite. Daylight hours are considerably less,
and so the recombination of ions into neutral molecules
increases. The seasonal effects are easily seen between the two

30

figures, with spring and autumn being essentially identical, and winter and summer having the greatest difference between them. These effects are multiplied when geographical variations are taken into account.

Tropical, or equatorial, zones receive a greater proportion of sunshine throughout the year than do the higher latitudes. Consequently, the summertime curve in Figure 8 predominates in these latitudes. Conversely, the higher latitudes show curves more closely akin to the winter curves. The Sun angle at midday grows proportionately less as the latitude is increased. So even though the poles may have six months of summer, the intensity of ultraviolet is reduced.

Because of the higher amount of ionization during summer it might be assumed that highest critical frequency would occur during that season. But just as a stone skipped across a pond loses energy each time it bounces, so does an electromagnetic wave when it strikes a conducting medium such as the F2 layer. As the ion density bends the incident wave back toward Earth, it extracts its price in energy. The absorption of the layer is at its highest during summer and so the critical frequency is lower.

Multi-year variations are, of course, due to the variations of the sunspot cycle. Figure 9 shows a graph of the first eleven cycles after the Maunder Minimum. One interesting feature of

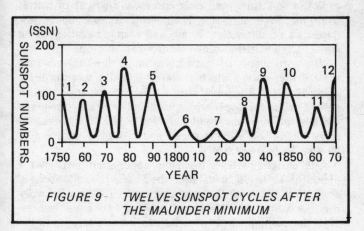

FIGURE 9   TWELVE SUNSPOT CYCLES AFTER THE MAUNDER MINIMUM

the graph is the somewhat slower decline of the sunspot numbers (SSN) after they have reached their peak in a particular cycle.

Another feature is the variation in the "11-year" cycle. The peak of Cycle 3 occurred about 8 years after the peak of Cycle 2, while the peak of Cycle 6 occurred about 16 years after the peak of Cycle 5. Often several periods of relatively low SSN will occur after several high SSN periods. These examples show that what most of us assume to be a stable, constant star is really a living, evolving stellar object which provides us with many useful things we take for granted.

Ionospheric Disturbances

Just as there are helpful disturbances (called storms) on the Earth which provide nourishing rain, sometimes these storms do more damage than good. The Sun is also plagued by disturbances which sometimes get out of hand. The three predominant types of disturbances which affect radio wave propagation are (1) the *solar flare*, (2) the *ionospheric storm*, and (3) the *sudden ionospheric disturbance (SID)*. Figure 10 shows how these disturbances reach the Earth.

Solar flares are believed to be sudden, and violent, changes in the magnetic fields in, and near, sunspots. They are explosive in nature, and eject enormous amounts of matter from the Sun's surface. Their ejecta is made up of vast quantities of ultraviolet, X-ray, and cosmic radiation, along with charged particles such as electrons and protons.

The particulate matter travels at much slower speeds than the radiative energy which is travelling at the speed of light. Approximately 8 minutes after a flare occurs, any radiative energy strikes the upper atmosphere and causes an increase in the absorption of the ionosphere and a SID. An increase in radio "noise" is also produced and is usually observed at frequencies below 300 MHz.

The charged particles reach the upper atmosphere over a period of 18 to 36 hours after the flare. They too increase absorption and cause ionospheric storms. They are primarily the reason for "radio blackouts" which last for more than one day. In addition, these particles can become trapped in the

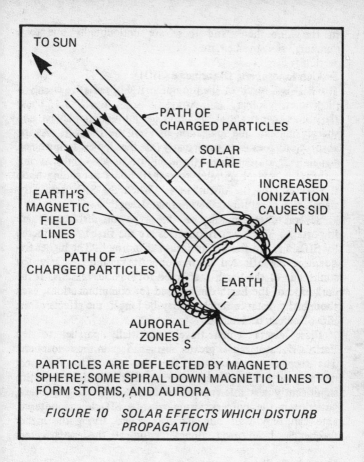

FIGURE 10   SOLAR EFFECTS WHICH DISTURB
PROPAGATION

Earth's magnetic field, and upon spiralling down the magnetic lines toward the poles cause the visual show we know as the Aurora Borealis, or in the southern hemisphere, the Southern Lights.

Often a flare is noticed on the Sun, but no particular disturbances are noted in our ionosphere. This is due to the path of ejection from the Sun. Unless the ejecta is on a path which carries it toward the Earth and its magnetosphere, it seldom affects us. Sometimes only minor disturbances will be noted in the ionosphere, and these are undoubtedly due to a "grazing" shot by the flare.

Sudden Ionospheric Disturbance (SID)

The SID is a result of the prompt arrival of radiative energy — ultraviolet, gamma, and X-rays — from the Sun. These radiations penetrate deep into the ionospheric layers and sharply increase the ionization of even the D layer. As the absorption goes up, particularly at the lower frequencies, signals fade out suddenly (in a minute or less) and may not return for several minutes to several hours depending upon the severity of the disturbance. When the SID passes, the signals slowly return to their normal strength.

Several characteristics of this type of disturbance are important. The lower frequencies are the first to be affected by SIDs and are the last to return to normal. The higher frequencies are affected in the opposite fashion. Only the sunlit side of the Earth is affected for obvious reasons. If the dark side of the Earth can be used for communications, even though the distance involved may be longer, the effects of the SID often can be avoided.

Flare ejecta which travels essentially parallel to the Earth's Equator causes greater disturbances in the ionosphere. The tropical, or equatorial, latitudes will suffer the most degradation in this circumstance. Higher latitudes can notice significantly less interruption in these cases. In any event, patience is the primary virtue when a SID is encountered. One can only wait out the disturbance, trying the higher frequencies from time to time since they are the least affected.

Ionospheric Storms

Ionospheric storms produce somewhat different results than those of the SID. Often the SID has completely disappeared by the time the particulate matter which causes the ionospheric storm arrives at the ionosphere. Because the particles move much slower than the radiation energy, they are deflected somewhat by the Earth's magnetosphere and move toward the poles. They disturb the upper regions of the ionosphere more as a result of this movement, primarily the F layer.

Depending upon their strength, the F layer may appear to vanish, split into several layers, or undergo rapid variations in ionized intensity. If the F layer disappears, then the predominant effect is loss of higher frequency capability. The other two effects can cause rapid fading or multiple echoes of signals.

If the effects are sufficiently strong, the E layer may be affected as well. This type of disturbance affects the dark side of the Earth as well as the sunlit side. Because of the deflection due to the magnetosphere, the ionospheric storm begins at the higher latitudes and then spreads lower depending upon the storm's severity.

During these disturbances, the use of lower frequencies should be tried first. Paths near the Equator may be less affected by these storms, and may provide adequate communications. These disturbances also last for several days longer than a SID, and patience is truly required to wait for the return of normal communications.

Polar Blackouts

Because the magnetosphere bends the paths of the slower moving ejecta which reach the Earth toward the poles, absorption at both polar areas increases when these energetic particles arrive to increase the ionization. This absorption can last from minutes to hours, and primarily affects the higher frequencies. As can be imagined, SIDs, ionospheric storms, and polar blackouts are often related sequentially. The SID and polar blackouts often occur together, with the following ionospheric storms increasing the auroral displays associated with these disturbances.

The same remedy is applicable to the polar blackout as with the ionospheric storm. Use lower frequencies, and use paths which are at the lower latitudes, since these are affected the least. Any path near, or through, a polar zone will be useless until the absorption abates.

Chapter 4

RADIO WAVE PROPAGATION

The propagation of electromagnetic waves provides the primary means of "wireless" communications both within and without the Earth's atmosphere. These waves are composed of both an electric field and a magnetic field as their name suggests. But it is the electric field which predominates at large distances from the transmitter of these waves. The energy in each wave is equally divided between the two fields, and their orientation determines whether they are *vertically* or *horizontally polarized.*

Figure 11 shows a representation of the two fields which are at right angles to one another travelling over the Earth. Since the *electric* lines of force are *vertical* the polarization of the wave is said to be *vertical.* The direction of travel of the wave in the figure is into the page away from the reader. The arrowheads indicate the *instantaneous* direction of each field.

Since radio waves (and all other electromagnetic waves) are alternating waves, the arrowheads will reverse themselves according to the *frequency* of the wave. That is, if the wave has a frequency of 500 kHz – or alternates at a rate of 500,000 cycles per second – then the arrowheads also change position at that rate. Reversal of the electric field causes the magnetic field to reverse as well, as the total wave propagates into space.

The polarization of the transmitting aerial determines the polarization of the radiated wave. A vertical aerial radiates a vertically polarized wave. Horizontally or vertically polarized waves are known as linearly polarized waves. For maximum receiving efficiency, the receiving aerial polarization should match the transmitting aerial. Reflectors of radio waves, such as the Earth and the ionosphere, are not perfect reflectors and there is some distortion of the polarization of a radio wave striking a reflector.

Linearly polarized waves become slightly elliptical when they reflect off the ionosphere for example. For long wavelengths this does not represent a problem, and a vertical aerial

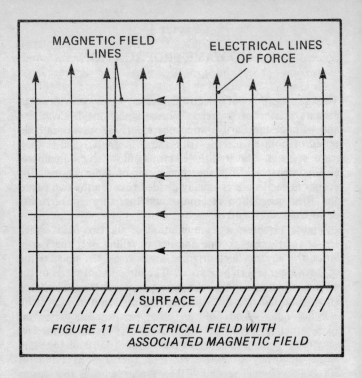

FIGURE 11   ELECTRICAL FIELD WITH
ASSOCIATED MAGNETIC FIELD

will still accept a wave which is radiated from a horizontal aerial. As the frequency rises, however, this type of *cross-polarization* becomes more and more noticeable.

At very high frequencies, a type of polarization known as *circular* polarization is often used. Aerials are wound in the form of a helix, or their radiated fields are rotated either electrically or mechanically to achieve circular polarization. As might be expected there is a *right-hand*, as well as a *left-hand* polarization available.

Opposite polarization at very high frequencies results in much more loss than at lower frequencies. A radio wave emitted by a right-hand polarized aerial will be received quite poorly by a left-hand polarized aerial, if at all. This effect is much less when linear-to-circular polarization is encountered. In this instance there is a loss of about one-half of the received signal by one or the other aerials.

If it were possible to have a point source (or isotropic source) as the transmitting aerial, then the waves would radiate outward in the form of a sphere, growing ever larger with time. The speed of propagation is the same as light in a vacuum, or about 300,000,000 metres per second. Propagation through a more dense medium is always less than that through a vacuum, and depends upon the density of the medium itself.

In the atmosphere, the reduction is relatively insignificant if the atmosphere is homogeneous. For radio frequencies up to 30 MHz, this is essentially true. For frequencies above 30 MHz however, rain, fog, and temperature changes can affect the *velocity of propagation*. These effects will be discussed in a later section.

Sky Wave Propagation

It is not possible to have a point source, or isotropic radiator, of radio waves as mentioned above. But even if it were, as the "wavefront" expands out spherically, it becomes closer and closer to a straight line. That is, the larger the radius of a circle, the closer the circumference approaches a straight line. This means that in ordinary circumstances, a propagated radio wave can be considered to be a *"plane wave"* as far as geometrical calculations are concerned.

Add to this that the ionospheric layers are themselves not smooth, perfectly reflecting surfaces, and it can be seen that some latitude is not only necessary but desirable for a practical understanding of radio wave propagation. In the following discussion, even more simplications will be made to illustrate the sky wave propagation mode.

Figure 12 shows a simplified geometry for *"1-Hop"* and *"2-Hop"* sky wave propagation between two points. Strictly speaking, the figure shows two *"rays"*, or straight lines, instead of waves travelling between two points by way of the ionosphere. There is no practical difference in presenting the wave as a straight line or ray. Note also that both the Earth's surface and the ionosphere are presented as flat, perfectly conducting surfaces to the rays.

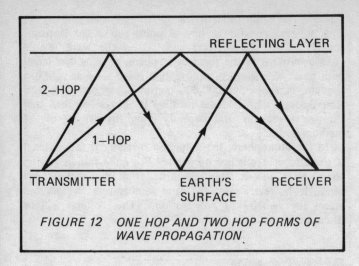

FIGURE 12   ONE HOP AND TWO HOP FORMS OF
WAVE PROPAGATION

The coincidence of the 1-Hop and 2-Hop rays at the receiving point illustrate a common feature of sky wave propagation. It is called *"multi-path propagation"* and occurs quite commonly. In some incidences it is responsible for fading conditions at the receiving location due to the time-of-travel differences between the two waves. On the other hand, "multi-hop" transmission such as the 2-Hop ray shown is the only way long distance, beyond the horizon, communications are possible. Both multi-path, and multi-hop transmissions will be dealt with in more detail later.

In geometric optics, when a ray of light goes from one transmission medium to another, a "bending" of the light ray takes place. The most common everyday example of this bending occurs when one places a drinking straw in a clear glass of water. Viewing the glass from the side shows an apparent bending of the straw at the water surface.

Figure 13A shows a typical example of this bending geometry. In Figure 13B the similar effect on a radio wave can be seen, but with one significant difference. In the water glass example, the surface of the water provides a sharp boundary between the water and the air above it. Because the ionospheric layer has a distinct depth, no such sharp boundary

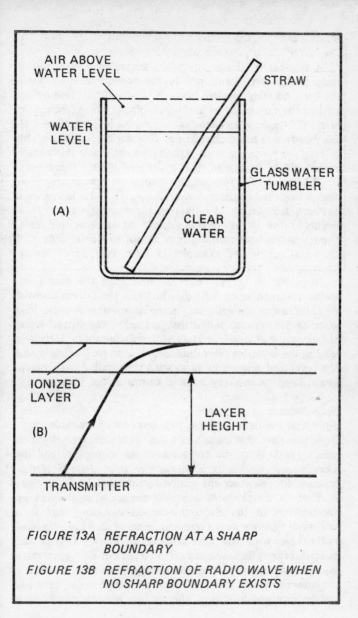

FIGURE 13A REFRACTION AT A SHARP
BOUNDARY

FIGURE 13B REFRACTION OF RADIO WAVE WHEN
NO SHARP BOUNDARY EXISTS

exists, and so the radio wave continues to be bent, or "*refracted*", as it passes through the ionospheric layer.

A number of things affect the ionospheric refraction of radio waves. As mentioned in the previous chapter, ionospheric sounding devices showed that critical frequencies existed for various layers in the ionosphere. These frequencies were the highest frequencies which would be returned to Earth, when radiated straight up. The angle of radiation also affects the propagation of sky waves since it was this phenomena which confirmed the existence of the ionosphere.

The degree of ionization also determines how much refraction is imparted to the incident radio wave. There is a relation between this degree of refraction and the angle at which it occurs known as the "*critical angle*". At or above this angle, the ray is not bent sufficiently to return to Earth. Figure 14 shows a number of examples of how radio waves can be propagated by the sky wave mode.

Note that at, or above, the critical angle the wave is no longer returned toward Earth. In 1927, the Danish scientist P. O. Pedersen investigating some seemingly unusual long distance propagation noted that just below the critical angle, the sky wave could be refracted just sufficiently to essentially stay in the layer for great distances. It then would finally exit the layer and resume its downward propagation. This high-angle, long distance ray became known as the Pedersen ray.

Skip Distance

Note that the figure also has two new concepts included in it. They are the "*skip angle*" and the "*skip distance*", both of which result from the curvature of the ionosphere and the Earth's surface. Figure 15 shows a more accurate picture of a curved Earth surface and a curved ionosphere.

There is a limit to how far one can see when standing on the surface of the Earth due to its curvature, and it is commonly known as the horizon. In theory, one can transmit radio waves over this range without difficulty. Beyond this range however, line-of-sight (LOS) conditions no longer exist. Because sky wave propagation is angle sensitive, there is a minimum distance below which the incident radio wave will not be returned to Earth. The distance between the horizon

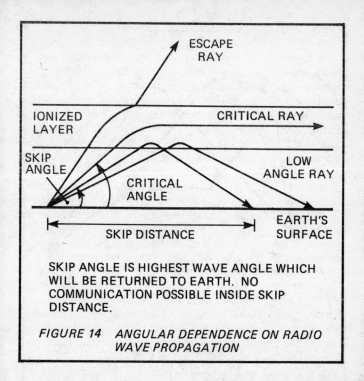

SKIP ANGLE IS HIGHEST WAVE ANGLE WHICH
WILL BE RETURNED TO EARTH. NO
COMMUNICATION POSSIBLE INSIDE SKIP
DISTANCE.

*FIGURE 14   ANGULAR DEPENDENCE ON RADIO
WAVE PROPAGATION*

and the nearest point at which radio waves are returned to
Earth, is known as the skip distance.

The LOS distance is most affected by the height of both
the transmitting and receiving aerials. Where this effect is
most noticeable is when one or both of the aerials is mounted
on an aircraft. Figure 16 shows how the LOS can be double
the distance to the horizon if both aerials are elevated. This
type of propagation becomes much more important as the
frequency is raised, and will be covered in more detail later. It
should be noted, however, that elevating the aerials does not
significantly affect the sky wave propagation distance since the
heights attainable are quite small when compared to the
height of the ionosphere.

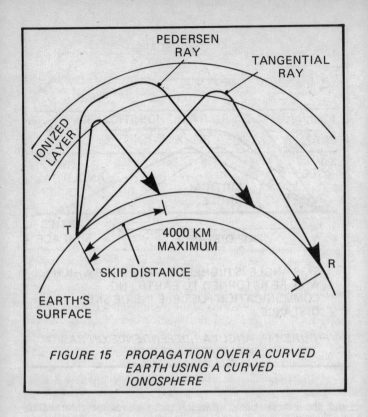

FIGURE 15   PROPAGATION OVER A CURVED
EARTH USING A CURVED
IONOSPHERE

Sky Wave Field Intensities

To this point only little has been said about the effects of
absorption on radio waves. Even though the ionosphere is
highly ionized, it is still not a perfect conductor. Each time a
radio wave "bounces", i.e. is reflected, or refracted, by the
ionosphere it loses energy. The energy is lost by the incident
wave due to the very fact of ionization in these upper layers.

The radio wave causes free electrons in an ionized region
to oscillate in simple harmonic motion with the frequency of
the wave. If the free electrons do not collide with anything,
the energy is simply exchanged between the two, and on the
average, no energy is lost as the wave leaves the ionized region.

44

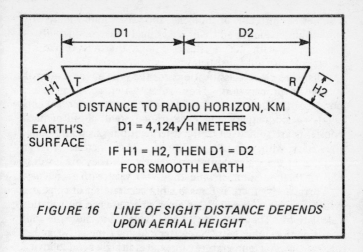

DISTANCE TO RADIO HORIZON, KM

$$D1 = 4,124\sqrt{H \text{ METERS}}$$

EARTH'S SURFACE

IF H1 = H2, THEN D1 = D2

FOR SMOOTH EARTH

FIGURE 16   LINE OF SIGHT DISTANCE DEPENDS UPON AERIAL HEIGHT

If on the other hand, the electrons collide with heavier atoms in the ionized region, they lose energy as the result of the collision. This energy is then subtracted from the radio wave since it is no longer available for free exchange between the two. If the frequency of the radio wave is much higher than the mean frequency of collisions between free electrons and heavier atoms the absorption will be less.

If the frequency of collisions is very high, then a great deal of energy will be absorbed from waves passing through the ionized regions. This is the reason for the higher absorption levels in the D and E layers. Since they are the last to be ionized, and the first to disappear at sunset, their "recombination rate" due to collisions is quite high.

Thus, they absorb more of the lower frequencies than they do the higher frequencies. After sunset, their disappearance removes these effects and there is an increase in the ability of lower frequencies (longer wavelengths) to propagate by way of the F layer. Again, tropical regions on the Earth are less affected because of the essentially higher solar radiation than the higher latitudes receive. Seasonal effects are most pronounced in the higher latitudes as a result.

In the case of multihop transmissions, the returning wave must bounce off the Earth's surface. Here absorption is due to a somewhat different phenomena, and varies quite widely with the terrain encountered. Not surprisingly the conductivity of Earth varies with the moisture content, thickness of the soil layers, and the soil consistency.

There are three classifications for the type of earth normally used in propagation. They are sea water, good earth, and poor earth. They may all be described by two physical constants — conductivity and dielectric constant. Both of these constants are somewhat difficult to determine accurately since they vary with weather conditions. They increase with an increase in the water content of the earth. They are lower in winter than in summer, and they also vary with frequency.

Fortunately, there is a reasonably accurate set of constants which provide a minimum of error when used in propagation calculations. They are presented in Table 1 and show the wide variation in conductivity. Sea water is highly conductive, and an increase in water temperature causes an even higher conductivity. The measure of *conductivity* used to be in mhos/metre, recalling that the "*mho*" is the reciprocal of the "*ohm*", or unit of resistivity, but the mho is now replaced by the "*siemens*".

Table 1
SOIL, OR EARTH, CONSTANTS FOR PROPAGATION

Ground Constants		
Terrain	*Dielectric Constant*	*Conductivity (mhos/m)*
Sea Water	80	5.0
Fresh Water	80	.005
Fertile Earth	15	.005
Rocky Earth	7	.001
Dry Soil	4	.001

The losses encountered when a wave is reflected from Earth are highly dependent upon what type of soil or water is encountered. Propagation over sea water is best for nearly all normal communications, with poorer soils absorbing a greater propagation of the incident wave as it is reflected. Soil effects will be discussed in more detail when ground wave propagation is covered due to their greater impact on this mode.

Maximum Usable Frequency (MUF)

All of the foregoing elements of radio wave propagation such as layer composition and heights, critical frequency, radiation angle, and losses, are necessary to have a clear picture of sky wave propagation using the ionosphere. They are used in determining which frequencies, or ranges of frequencies, are most useful over any given path during day or night at any time of the year.

For any given path between two points on Earth, there is a Maximum Usable Frequency, or MUF, which is closely related to the critical frequency. As will be recalled, the critical frequency was measured by directing the wave vertically toward the ionosphere. This is not a very useful frequency for most purposes. Instead, radiation at some lower angle is necessary to provide the proper refraction geometry for the distance involved.

Figure 17 shows a geometrical equivalent of the path from the transmitter, T, and the receiver, R. Here H is the lower edge of the ionospheric layer, and D is an arbitrary distance between the two locations. In the figure, h^1 is called the *"virtual height"*, because geometrically the reflection point of the wave appears to be P. In reality, there is no single reflection point, rather the wave is refracted through the layer, and the actual height, h, occurs at point C. The virtual height is used when formal mathematical calculations are made for scientific and engineering uses.

Of paramount importance is the angle X, at the transmission point, formed by the lines TR and TP. A trigonometric function called the *"cosecant"* is used to help determine the MUF. The formula is as follows:

$$MUF = f_{crit} (\csc X),$$

47

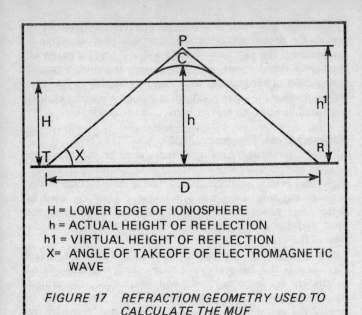

H = LOWER EDGE OF IONOSPHERE
h = ACTUAL HEIGHT OF REFLECTION
h1 = VIRTUAL HEIGHT OF REFLECTION
X = ANGLE OF TAKEOFF OF ELECTROMAGNETIC
    WAVE

*FIGURE 17   REFRACTION GEOMETRY USED TO
CALCULATE THE MUF*

where

f_{crit} = critical frequency, and
csc = cosecant (abbreviation), and
X = angle of radiation.

Without getting too deeply involved with the mathematics of the problem, the cosecant is equal to unity, or one, when X is 90 degrees. Therefore the MUF equals the critical frequency, which is another way of defining the critical frequency.

As the angle X becomes less than 90 degrees, the value of the cosecant increases, so that as the angle at which the wave strikes the ionosphere becomes smaller, the MUF increases. For example, at an angle X = 45 degrees, the cosecant of X = 1.414. The MUF is therefore 41.4% greater than the critical frequency at T. If the critical frequency at T = 10 MHz, then at a radiation angle of 45 degrees, the MUF = 14.14 MHz.

48

If it were possible to operate at the MUF at all times, it would be the best of all circumstances. Received signal levels would be at their highest because ionospheric losses would be at their lowest levels. But since the MUF is a representation of the level of ionization, it too has diurnal, seasonal, geographical, and cyclical variations exactly in step with the ionosphere.

Note that transmitted power has not been a factor in any of the calculations so far. Except for certain circumstances, it is not a factor. Either the wave is returned from the ionosphere or it is not. It is dependent only upon the MUF value, and the condition of the ionosphere.

It is possible to operate below the MUF, and indeed this is often done. Shortwave broadcast stations are normally assigned fixed bands or frequencies for their transmissions. Their assignments are often made within several bands so that as the MUF varies, they may shift their operations to the most optimum frequencies for the desired coverage. A similar situation is found in the radio amateur world, where operation is only allowed in fixed frequency bands.

It is possible to do some degree of predicting the value of the MUF for given paths or areas. The International Telecommunications Union (Geneva) publishes an "Atlas of Ionospheric Characteristics" which provide data on world-wide values of critical frequencies. These data are calculated for a standard distance of 4000 km, and graphical means are used to calculate the MUFs for lesser distances. Very little mathematics are required for these calculations.

These methods of predictions do have some simplifications built into them for ease of calculation. The 4000 km is a standard distance based upon a radiation angle of 0 degrees, or tangent to the Earth's surface, and an ionospheric height of 250 km. It is the longest 1-Hop distance possible. Any path longer than 4000 km must be done in multiple hops.

The Earth and the ionosphere are assumed to be perfect spheres, and the degree of ionization is considered homogeneous. No unusual effects are assumed to exist such as sporadic-E propagation, or the Pedersen ray phenomenon. Precise adherence to the MUF is neither possible, nor is it necessary. All that is required to operate on such a frequency are that variations in the ionosphere are minimized, as well as any losses which may occur. These frequencies are called the "optimum traffic frequencies".

Optimum Traffic Frequency (FOT)

Sometimes called the "optimum working frequency (OWF)", the *optimum traffic frequency* is normally abbreviated FOT from the French *frequence optimum de travail.* However it is pronounced, or abbreviated, it is selected to be just that — an optimum frequency. One free of instantaneous variations associated with the ionosphere, yet high enough to provide maximum signal strength at the desired receiving points.

It is normally taken as 85% of the MUF. This will vary as the MUF varies, but is not critical unless there is a wide change in the value of the MUF. A wide swing of the MUF occurs diurnally at sunrise and sunset. The normal procedure in these cases is to have a daytime and a night-time frequency, and switch between one or the other as the situation demands.

Lowest Usable Frequency (LUF)

The *lowest usable frequency* is not primarily dependent upon the ionosphere as is the MUF. Although the radiated power of the transmitting station does not affect the MUF, it is a primary component in determining the LUF. The LUF is defined as the lowest frequency for which the received signal intensity equals the required field intensity for satisfactory reception of the desired signal over a given path.

At the receiver site the required field intensity of a given signal depends upon:

1. The receiving aerial
2. Local noise levels
3. The path distance
4. Absorption losses.

The aerial used at the receiving site will be most efficient if it is "resonant" at the desired frequency. By "resonant" we mean it is sized to a proper length to absorb a maximum amount of the desired signal it intercepts. How this is done is not a proper topic in this book, and is covered quite well elsewhere.

Local noise levels can be both man-made and of atmospheric origin. Unless they are properly filtered and shielded, many man-made noise sources can cause difficulty in reception. Such devices are electrical generators, automotive ignition systems, electrically powered tools, lamp dimmers, and faulty thermostats on aquariums for example. Chapter 6 covers noise and its affects more fully.

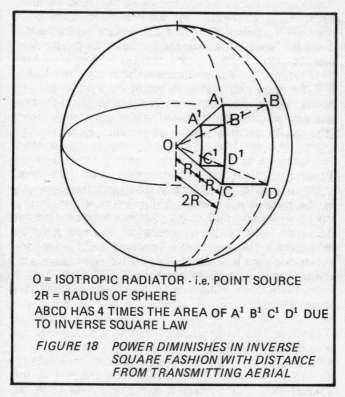

O = ISOTROPIC RADIATOR - i.e. POINT SOURCE
2R = RADIUS OF SPHERE
ABCD HAS 4 TIMES THE AREA OF $A^1 B^1 C^1 D^1$ DUE TO INVERSE SQUARE LAW

FIGURE 18   POWER DIMINISHES IN INVERSE SQUARE FASHION WITH DISTANCE FROM TRANSMITTING AERIAL

The path distance over which a signal must travel causes it to diminish in power level in what is called the "inverse square law". Figure 18 shows our fictitious isotropic radiator which radiates a spherical wave equally out into space. At a distance R from the aerial, the field intensity is "E" volts per square metre (v/m^2). At a distance of 2R, our square metre has become 4 square metres as the figure shows. This increase in area is due to the mathematical fact that the surface area of a sphere varies as the "square" of the radius. But the radiated power has not changed therefore it must be spread over four times the area, and has thus diminished to one-fourth its value at R.

The longer the path then, the weaker the signal becomes, and it also is affected by the last item listed — absorptive losses. We saw how the D and E layers are predominantly absorptive layers. The lower the frequency the greater these losses become. There is some loss in the F layer, as we have seen, but it is of a lesser magnitude than the lower layers.

If the signal path is through one of the polar zones, then auroral absorption must be considered as well. Here the sunspot numbers impact the amount of absorption, since higher SSNs usually result in greater absorption. Note that this absorption is not due to SIDs, ionospheric storms, or other flare-induced activity. This type of activity simply increases the already present "natural" absorption of the ionosphere.

The amount of signal initially radiated therefore impacts on the received signal level. The problem of transmitting aerial resonance is usually not a problem since it must present the proper "look" to the transmitter for maximum power to be radiated by the aerial. If a directional aerial is used for transmitting then receiving stations off the proper angle will, of course, receive lesser amounts of signal.

For example, a broadcast quality signal may require 12 kHz for good fidelity reception. A simple Morse Code signal has a much narrower channel requirement, perhaps only 1 kHz. In this instance, the broadcast signal requires approximately ten times the signal strength at the receiver than the Morse signal does. This is due to the fact that the wider the "bandwidth" required at the receiver, the more noise is accepted by the receiver. And so the "signal-to-noise" ratio must be higher for the same quality of reception of the wider signal. This will also be delved into in a later chapter.

As a result of the dependence of the LUF more on the actual physical equipment, and aerials used, than on the ionosphere it can be seen that it is quite possible for the LUF to

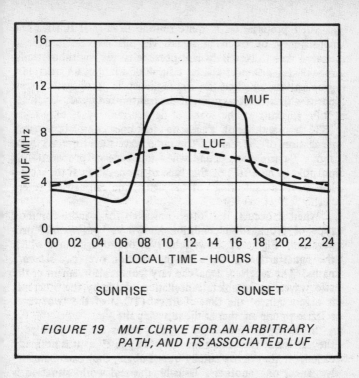

FIGURE 19   MUF CURVE FOR AN ARBITRARY
PATH, AND ITS ASSOCIATED LUF

exceed the MUF. Figure 19 shows a typical curve of MUF
with an accompanying LUF curve which exceeds the MUF
toward sunrise and sunset. During these periods, communications over the path is impossible. Only an increase in radiated
power by the transmitter, or a lowering of the noise level at
the receiver location, can lower the LUF sufficiently to allow
communications to take place.

Multi-hop Propagation

Figure 12 showed both 1-Hop and 2-Hop propagation path
examples. It was further noted that 4000 km is about the
limit for 1-Hop propagation due to the "take-off" angle of the
radio wave being 0-degrees, or tangent to the Earth's surface.
For distances over 4000 km then, it is necessary to utilize
more than one hop to complete the path.

Such propagation is quite routine in normal times. The consistency of receiving signals via this method is demonstrated daily. Not only is it possible to use multi-hop transmission for distances greater than 4000 km, but under certain propagation conditions, round-the-world propagation can occur with little absorption of the transmitted wave.

Propagating at the speed of light, a radio wave only takes 133 thousandths of a second for one complete circumnavigation of the Earth. The radio wave therefore can make about 7½ trips per second when this type of propagation is possible. The effect of this type of propagation at the receiving site is a "smearing" of the signal, and can cause a severe "echo" effect to exist.

When it occurs, it is often mistaken for a more common type of propagation condition known as "*multi-path*" propagation. Figure 12 showed this type of propagation in which the signal arrives at the receiving location over two *separate* paths. The received signal can vary from reinforcement of the two waves, to complete cancellation of one by the other. It is a function of the time-of-arrival (TOA) of the two waves relative to one another at the receiving site.

In theory the power in the two waves can be doubled if they arrive at the same time — or "in-phase" as it is normally called. If they arrive totally out-of-phase, they can completely cancel one another. Usually, the real world situation is somewhere in between, and various degrees of fading occur. Depending upon the volatility of the ionosphere, fading can be slow and deep, or it can be rapid enough to cause a flutter effect to be heard.

At very high frequencies, such as those used by television signals, a visual indication of this flutter effect is often seen when an aircraft flies between the television station and the television receiving aerial. Due to the signal reflection off the aircraft, two (or more) signals appear at the receiving aerial and cause the picture to fade in and out — sometimes quite rapidly.

At very high frequencies, a fixed object will reflect a portion of the television signal toward the receiving aerial. Since the object is not in motion, the time delay will be fixed, and "ghosts" will appear on the television screen. This is simply a visual example of multi-path propagation, and generally it can be dealt with by re-orientation of the receiving aerial.

At short-wave broadcast frequencies, as well as radio amateur frequencies, the solution is to increase the listening, or operating, frequency. This technique puts the listening frequency closer to the MUF which reduces losses. In addition, the higher frequency passes through any lower layer such as the E-layer and any contribution by this layer to the multipath effect is eliminated.

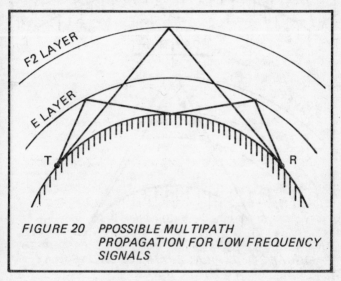

FIGURE 20   PPOSSIBLE MULTIPATH
PROPAGATION FOR LOW FREQUENCY
SIGNALS

Figure 20 shows how an E-layer signal can be reflected over a multi-hop path at the same time as the same signal is reflected from the F layer so that both arrive at the receiving aerial simultaneously. By raising the frequency so that it is not reflected by the E layer, this multi-hop path is eliminated.

One-way signal propagation is also a common phenomena in the radio amateur world. Here the desire to communicate bi-laterally between two radio amateurs is thwarted because one can hear the other but the reverse is not true. Often this is caused by reflection of a signal off the "*top*" of a layer which exists only at one end of the path. Figure 21A shows

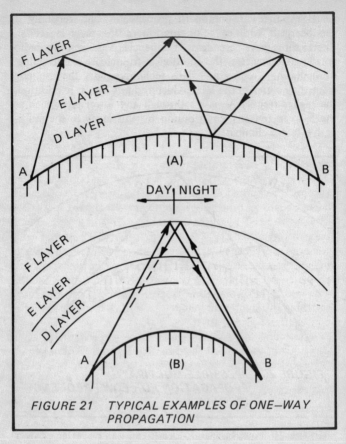

FIGURE 21   TYPICAL EXAMPLES OF ONE—WAY
PROPAGATION

how this can happen, and in this case it is a sporadic-E layer
which is the catalyst.

The signal from A is reflected normally from the F layer,
but due to the existence of a sporadic-E layer in the direction
of B, it is reflected off the top of the sporadic-E layer back
toward the F layer. It then is reflected again down toward B
who receives the signal. Reversing the transmission path is
another story. The signal from B strikes the F layer and is
reflected back down, but the sporadic-E layer does not exist in
the signal's path. Hence it strikes the Earth and must pass

back *through* the sporadic-E layer which may absorb most of its energy. As a result the signal from B may be too weak to be heard at A.

Figure 21B shows how propagation across a day—night boundary can also cause one-way propagation. The transmission from A to B arrives without problem, but the return path has excessive absorption in passing through the D and E layers. As a result, it is not above the noise at the receiver located at A.

Trans-equatorial Propagation (TE)
There are several modes of radio wave propagation which seem to defy the normal explanations of ionospheric propagation. Trans-equatorial propagation is one of these modes.

First noticed by radio amateurs over forty years ago, it seemed to contradict the notion that the MUF must be below the critical frequency. To be sure, there has been a postulated highest possible frequency (HPF) which is 15% higher than the predicted MUF, but only occurs 10% of the time. But this new mode of propagation appeared almost simultaneously on three different paths, and was verified by stations on all continents.

The mode was a north—south mode of propagation across the Equator, and often for distances up to 8000 km. It was first noticed during sunspot cycle 18 in 1947, one of the highest sunspot cycles on record. In Europe the path extends from Southern Europe to Southern Africa. Similar paths extend from Puerto Rico to Argentina, and Japan to Australia, on the other continents. It received its name Trans-Equatorial, or TE mode, because the way it operates.

TE frequencies are always at least 1.5 times the predicted MUF for these paths. Because of the higher density of ionization in the equatorial regions, regardless of season, year-round MUFs in this region remain quite high. During night-time hours, the TE mode frequencies also remain quite high despite the fact that the MUF is always less during this time.

But the ionosphere is not a perfect sphere with a constant density. At the Equator, it is much thicker, and while the normal MUF varies with solar activity, it does not do so in the usual manner of F layer variations. At sunset, the ionization density begins to take over when the F layer propagation begins to fade out. The TE range is about 4000 km on either side of the *geomagnetic* equator. Because the Earth's magnetic poles are not coincident with the *geophysical* poles, the geomagnetic equator is also tilted with respect to the geophysical equator.

This factor is the reason for the north—south end points to be different in different regions of the world. In the European area, the TE mode reaches the United Kingdom. In the Americas, only the southern portion of the United States, Puerto Rico, and Mexico benefit from the TE mode of propagation. As a result of this, radio amateurs in Zimbabwe, Cyprus, and the European continent instigated studies of this mode which helped provide technically sound explanations for the TE mode of propagation.

Their work showed that signals entering the areas of much greater ionized density, at the most favourable angle, often were returned to Earth at much longer distances than could be explained by simple refraction geometry. The signals had to cross the Equator very close to right-angles, although some variation up to 20 degrees was still possible. The phenomenon of TE mode propagation supports a wide frequency range, and in some instances the range has extended from 14 MHz up to 144 MHz — or a ten to one ratio.

It is predominantly a night-time phenomenon, and usually occurs over periods of medium to high solar activity. Although not limited to any particular season, more TE openings occur during spring and autumn. At these times the Earth's axis is perpendicular to the plane of the ecliptic, and so ionization of the upper atmosphere is an absolute maximum. Figure 22 shows the Europe—Africa paths involved during this propagation mode. The primary zones are zones of higher signal strength than the secondary zones. Under the proper conditions, reception can be quite adequate in the secondary zones.

Grey Line Propagation

This is another mode of ionospheric propagation which was discovered by radio amateurs about 1975. The term *grey line* refers to what astronomers call the "terminator" on the Earth, Moon, and other interstellar bodies which are illuminated by

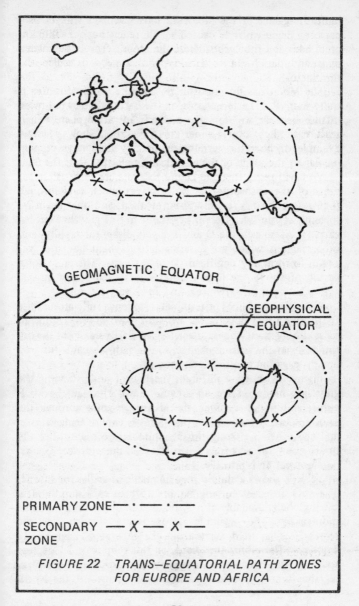

GEOMAGNETIC EQUATOR

GEOPHYSICAL
EQUATOR

PRIMARY ZONE — · — · —

SECONDARY — X — X —
ZONE

FIGURE 22   TRANS—EQUATORIAL PATH ZONES
FOR EUROPE AND AFRICA

light. A glance at the Moon on most evenings will shows a crescent shape which is caused by our seeing both the illuminated side, and the dark side, of the Moon. The line between light and dark — a twilight type of zone — is called the terminator.

The Moon has no atmosphere, and the terminator area is quite narrow. The terminator on the Earth is somewhat more diffuse because we do have a significant atmosphere which scatters the light over a wider area. Figure 23 shows a simple example of how the terminator, or grey line, stays perpendicular to the plane of the ecliptic as the Earth orbits the Sun.

You will recall that the D and E layers are responsible for most of the absorption of radio waves which pass through them. But these layers disappear at night, and only begin re-forming at sunrise. Herein lies the secret of grey line propagation. At sunset, the D and E layers disappear rapidly, and other regions which are entering into daylight have not yet begun to form any significant D or E layers. Therefore for a period of about one hour around sunrise and sunset, propagation between these two regions can be very efficient.

Since the grey line, or terminator, extends fully around the Earth, it is often possible for around-the-world propagation to exist during these times. Because the Earth's axis shifts continuously as the seasons change, so the paths available for grey line propagation also shift continuously.

Figure 24 shows a different method of understanding the grey line mode. Here an area is drawn through the MUF curve, and it can be seen the MUFs are going through the same frequency range when one point is experiencing sunrise, and the other is passing through sunset into night. For the brief hour or so during which this coincidence occurs, communication is possible.

Table 2 shows a simple grey line table of angles for sunrise. The data are given for the 1st and 15th of each month. If a small globe is available, it may be used to understand the table more easily. For example, on January 1 of each year, the North Pole is tilted away from the Sun at an angle of 23 degrees. Therefore, the plane of the ecliptic is 23 degrees *south* of the Equator, or tangent to the Tropic of Capricorn. At the summer solstice, approximately June 21, the North

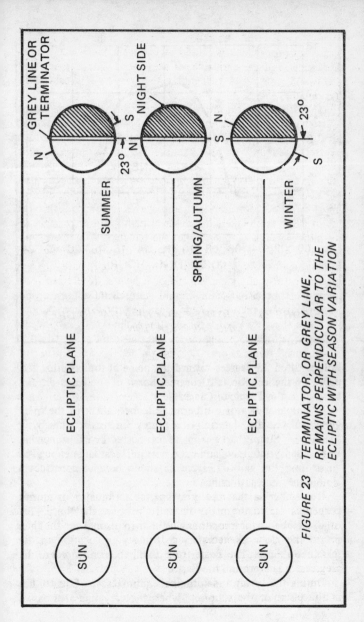

FIGURE 23 TERMINATOR, OR GREY LINE,
REMAINS PERPENDICULAR TO THE
ECLIPTIC WITH SEASON VARIATION

61

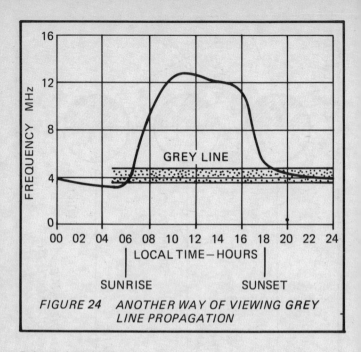

FIGURE 24   ANOTHER WAY OF VIEWING GREY
LINE PROPAGATION

Pole is tilted 23 degrees toward the plane of the ecliptic. The plane of the ecliptic is 23 degrees *north* of the Equator, and tangent to the Tropic of Cancer.

A simple indicator can be made to be used with the small globe to visually determine the grey line path from your location.   Simply take a piece of poster board somewhat larger than your globe, and cut a hole in it just large enough to fit around the globe.   Figure 25 shows how to construct a simple grey line path indicator.

Remembering that the grey line, or terminator, is *always* perpendicular to the plane of the ecliptic, set the North Pole of the globe at the proper angle for the seasonal time.   Then rotate the globe as necessary to bring your location to the terminator line.   The poster board will then show where the grey line area is around the Earth.

During the spring and autumnal equinoxes, the Equator lies in the plane of the ecliptic.   When the grey line area passes

62

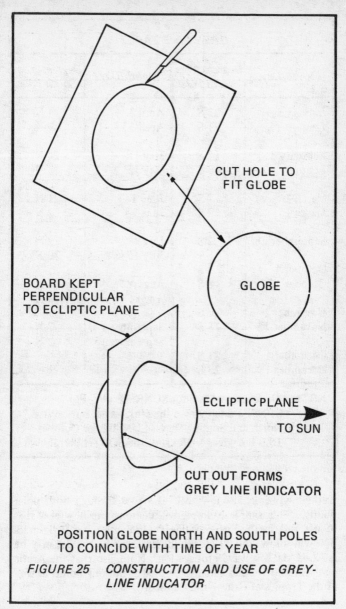

CUT HOLE TO FIT GLOBE

GLOBE

BOARD KEPT PERPENDICULAR TO ECLIPTIC PLANE

ECLIPTIC PLANE

TO SUN

CUT OUT FORMS GREY LINE INDICATOR

POSITION GLOBE NORTH AND SOUTH POLES TO COINCIDE WITH TIME OF YEAR

FIGURE 25   CONSTRUCTION AND USE OF GREY-LINE INDICATOR

Table 2
GREY LINE TABLE

Month/Day	Degrees from North Pole	Month/Day	Degrees from South Pole
January 1	23 S	April 3	4 N
January 15	21 S	April 15	9 N
February 1	17 S	May 1	14 N
February 15	13 S	May 15	18 N
March 1	7 S	June 1	21 N
March 15	2 S	June 15	22 N
September 28	2 S	July 1	22 N
		July 15	20 N
October 1	3 S		
October 15	8 S	August 1	17 N
		August 15	13 N
November 1	14 S		
November 15	18 S	September 1	7 N
		September 15	2 N
December 1	21 S		
December 15	23 S		

NOTE: The above table is for SUNRISE use. For SUNSET simply read the same angle, but reverse North and South. That is SUNSET for October 15 is 8 degrees NORTH of the SOUTH POLE.

through your location, it will also pass through both polar points. This simple example will demonstrate how easy it is to use this method of grey line determination. A little practice will allow you to quickly determine which areas may be reached via sky wave propagation. Note also that the Arctic and Antarctic circles can also be used as limiting points as well as the Tropics of Cancer and Capricorn.

The determination of the grey line area for sunset is just as easy. The values in the table need only be reversed from North to South. That is, if an angle in the table is "north" for sunrise, it will be "south" for sunset. This means that there is a different grey line path at sunset than the one which occurs at sunrise. This is true except for the spring and autumnal equinoxes when the polar axis of the Earth is perpendicular to the plane of the ecliptic.

Because of the limited time, and variable azimuths, which accompany the grey line period for communication, a directional aerial is of considerable help. An aerial which is vertically polarized will be useful in any event, although it will not provide gain as directional aerials often do. If there is a favoured direction for listening, then the grey line calculator will provide the optimum times of year to monitor the desired path.

Ground Wave Propagation

Although there has been some confusion in the past over what exactly constitutes "ground wave" propagation, it has generally come to include all radio wave propagation which does not involve the ionosphere. Yet even this definition is not very satisfactory. In this section only ground wave propagation by Medium (MF) and Low Frequencies (LF) are considered, since Chapter 5 covers non-ionospheric wave propagation including the higher frequency ranges.

In the early days of radio, before the discovery of the ionosphere, the only way to achieve communications over greater distances was to erect larger aerials and increase the transmitted power. As can be imagined, this has limitations not only in the size of aerials, but in power capability as well. It was also discovered that higher frequencies do not propagate well over the Earth due primarily to increasing losses as the frequency is raised.

The absorption of LF, and MF, signals which did reach the D and E layers increased as the frequency decreased so that long-distance signalling became limited to the high frequencies (HF) almost exclusively. The LF and MF ranges, however, have attributes which make them very suitable for communications over distances and paths which are difficult for frequencies in the HF range to accomplish.

Ground Wave Field Intensities

The strength of a ground wave signal depends upon the type of terrain, the path between the transmitter and receiver, transmitted power, the frequency used, the type of transmitting aerial, and the heights of both the transmitting and receiving aerials. At distances beyond the horizon, the curvature of the Earth's surface hides the two aerials from one another unless they are sufficiently elevated to have line-of-sight (LOS) conditions between them.

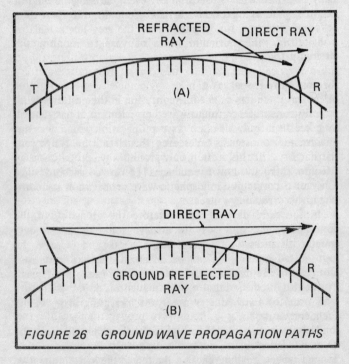

FIGURE 26   GROUND WAVE PROPAGATION PATHS

Figure 26A shows the situation where the receiving aerial is below the horizon. Reception may still be possible because the radio LOS is slightly greater than the visual LOS due to refraction by the atmosphere of the radio wave. This refraction is akin to ordinary optical refraction of light waves and is not similar to that which occurs in the ionosphere.

Figure 26B shows the two paths between transmitting and receiving aerials which do have a LOS condition existing between them. Here two ray paths are possible. The *direct*, or *space*, wave travels directly between the aerials. The *ground reflected* wave reaches the receiving aerial after bouncing off the Earth's surface.

In this instance, a similar condition exists as in the case of multi-path transmission discussed in a previous section. Depending upon the path lengths, the signal at the receiving aerial may vary from reinforcement by both waves, to cancellation of all or part of the signal.

Note that the receiving aerial does not need to be mounted on the surface, but rather, can be on a low flying aircraft. For short distances, and altitudes of only a few hundred metres, the ground reflected ray can be comparable in strength to the direct wave. The lower the frequency the less the difference in path distances, and consequently, the possibility of destructive interference is less.

Ground wave signals are strong when the conductivity of the Earth's surface is high. Sea water has the highest conductivity, with rocky and dry soil having the least conductivity. The situation here is the same as discussed in a previous section on multi-hop transmission. Whenever an electromagnetic wave strikes or is propagated over a specific terrain, the characteristics of the terrain determine the losses and reflectivity of the terrain to the incident wave.

Ground Wave Propagation Frequencies

Contrary to the use of designators such as MUF, and LUF, which are common to sky wave propagation, there are no such frequencies for ground wave propagation. Since the ionosphere is not involved, the highest frequency which may be used is dependent upon the distance between the transmitting and receiving points. As the distance increases the rate of absorption rises for a given frequency, until at last, there is insufficient signal strength for the signal to be received adequately.

Although the losses for frequencies below 1.5 MHz are less as the frequency goes down, the limiting factor for a "lowest" frequency is more dependent upon the inability to build large enough aerial structures for efficient radiation, and the large components needed for the equipment itself. A distinct limitation on aerial height also occurs due to excessive polarization losses with horizontal antennas.

Most ground wave transmitters, such as those found in LF and MF broadcasting for example, are used with vertical aerials. The vertically polarized signal is less affected by the terrain type than is the horizontally polarized type. Horizontal aerials also require a minimum height above ground to be effective, and normally require two supports. It is easier and more efficient to use a single vertical aerial with a wire ground-screen which can be simply laid on the surface, or buried a few centimetres below the surface.

The range from 1.5 to 30 MHz can be used for ground wave propagation but brings with it some additional problems. In addition to greater losses at the higher frequencies, the fact that the radiated signal cannot be confined close to the surface causes multi-path problems. Since these frequencies propagate very well in the sky wave mode, at certain distances the inadvertent radiation which strikes the ionosphere is brought back to interfere with the desired ground wave, and this can cause severe fading problems.

Throughout this book the figures have portrayed the radiated wave as a "ray", or straight line. It is not possible to confine radio waves into straight lines, as it is for example, in lasers or other optical transmission systems. Consequently, radiation from the normal aerial is spread across what mathematicians call a "solid angle". That is radio waves are three-dimensional when they are radiated, having a width and depth. Figure 27A shows a typical vertical antenna used in ground wave propagation, and its *"radiation pattern"*. Note that the radiation pattern has a "null" directly overhead, but fills out a broad angular area down to 0 degrees.

Figure 27B shows how a portion of this pattern strikes the ionosphere and is reflected back to Earth in a normal fashion. It covers a broad area upon return to the surface. If a portion of this area overlaps the ground wave path, then a multi-path

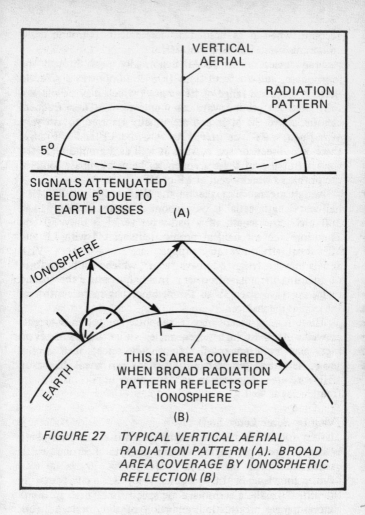

FIGURE 27   TYPICAL VERTICAL AERIAL
RADIATION PATTERN (A). BROAD
AREA COVERAGE BY IONOSPHERIC
REFLECTION (B)

condition exists with all of its inherent problems, such as
fading and interference. Any fluctuation of the ionosphere
will be immediately apparent at the receiving location. Since
aerials may be constructed in many sizes and shapes, the
radiation patterns will be dependent upon the geometry of
the aerial itself. These are factors which must be taken into

account when it is desired to . implement a ground wave communications link below 30 MHz.

Frequencies above 30 MHz normally pass through the ionosphere, and are limited to LOS conditions as a rule. So there is a second range of frequencies which may be successfully used for ground wave communications. These frequencies lie above 30 MHz and are usually referred to as *"very high frequencies"*, or *VHF*. As with the LF and MF range, there is a direct, or space, wave as well as a ground reflected wave. But use of these frequencies helps eliminate some of the problems which occur at LF or MF.

Aerials are much smaller in the VHF range. A 30 MHz, half-wavelength aerial is only about 5 metres in length. At 300 MHz, the length of a half-wave aerial is only 50 cm. Therefore the mechanical problems associated with LF and MF aerial structures and supports are non-existent. VHF aerials may be designed to have "gain", which results in a form of focusing of radiated power. This helps reduce the ground reflected wave strength so the designer has more control of the circuit mechanics.

These smaller aerials may be supported at optimum heights as well. At these higher frequencies, other unique disadvantages play important roles. Atmospheric effects such as rain, snow, sleet, and temperature inversions can wreak havoc on VHF circuits. Polarization becomes more important at these frequencies as well.

Tying Up Some Loose Ends

The portion of the radio spectrum which uses the ionosphere is but a small part of an electromagnetic spectrum which extends from the AC mains frequency of 50 Hz up well beyond the visual light frequencies. Table 3 is a chart showing the extent of the electromagnetic spectrum. There are some general ranges of the radio portion of the total spectrum which have specific capabilities, and have been further developed to enhance these capabilities.

The range of frequencies from 0.03 to 3000 MHz are normally used for communications purposes. Frequencies above 3000 MHz are generally used for non-communications purposes such as radar, aircraft navigational facilities, satellite

Table 3
MORE COMMON BANDS IN THE
FREQUENCY SPECTRUM

Band Description	MHz	Amateur Bands	Broadcast Bands	T.V. Bands
VERY LOW FREQUENCY (V.L.F.)	0.003 — 0.03			
LOW FREQUENCY (L.F.)	0.03 — 0.3		• LW Band	
MEDIUM FREQUENCY (M.F.)	0.3 — 3	• 160M	MW Band • 120M	
HIGH FREQUENCY (H.F.)	3 — 30	• 80M • 40M • 29.5M • 20M • 16.5M • 15M • CB • 12M • 10M	• 90M • 75m • 60M • 49M • 41M • 31M • 25M • 19M • 16M • 13M • 11M	
VERY HIGH FREQUENCY (V.H.F.)	30 — 300	• 6M • 4M • 2M	FM Band III	
ULTRA HIGH FREQUENCY (U.H.F.)	300 — 3000	• CB • 70CM • 23CM • 13CM		• Band IV • Band V
SUPER HIGH FREQUENCY (S.H.F.)	3000 — 30000			• Band VI Satellite
EXTRA HIGH FREQUENCY (E.H.F.)	30000 — 300000			

NOTE: This table illustrates only some of the more common bands in the frequency spectrum. It is not drawn to scale.

radio links, and general research purposes. Table 3 shows the various bands into which the frequency spectrum has been divided up to 30,000 MHz.

Frequencies from 0.03 to 0.3 MHz are normally used for long-distance ground wave communications, especially in regions where ionospheric blackouts are common. As we have seen these blackouts commonly occur in auroral areas, and at high latitudes. The ionosphere is considerably more variable at these latitudes.

Frequencies from 0.1 to 3.0 MHz find their main use in ground wave transmission over moderate distances over water and somewhat shorter distances over land. Radio navigation by way of Loran-C is a typical example of this type of use. Loran-C operates at 0.1 MHz and transmits a series of coded pulses from master–slave combinations. Vessels and aircraft which are equipped to receive these transmissions use them for locating their own positions on the Earth's surface.

Although the bands in Table 3 show sharp dividing lines, in reality there are "gray areas" which overlap from one band to another. For example, low frequency broadcasting extends well down into this band toward 0.1 MHz. It also extends upward toward 1.5 MHz. This is because the range of frequencies from 1.0 to 3.0 MHz are well suited for sky wave transmission up to 320 km in distance during the night. The LF and MF broadcast ranges straddle one grey area where ground wave propagation predominates at the lower end of the range, and the sky wave predominates at the upper end.

In the 3.0 to 30.0 MHz HF range, the 3.0 to 8.0 MHz range will provide daytime sky wave propagation out to about 320 km. For long distance sky wave propagation, the 3.0 to 12.0 MHz HF range is very effective during the night. During the day, the 6.0 to 25.0 MHz range is normally used over these long distances since the absorption is lower as we have seen.

The frequencies above 30.0 MHz have been devoted to a variety of uses, most of them LOS transmissions, such as FM broadcasting, TV broadcasting, and general communications uses such as microwave transmission links for long distance telephone use. As science and technology progresses, these frequencies have found many more space age uses, not only in the measurement and navigation fields, such as radar and microwave landing systems for aircraft, but communications between Earth and her astronauts. At the extreme end of the electromagnetic spectrum, the laser has found many uses from the medical field, manufacturing, and earthquake measurements and prediction.

The next chapter will cover some of the more exotic forms of radio wave propagation such as tropospheric scatter communications (tropo), satellite communications, meteorite communications, and moonbounce or Earth—Moon—Earth (EME) as it is also known.

Chapter 5

NON-IONOSPHERIC PROPAGATION

The discussion of radio wave propagation up to this point has concerned itself to a large extent with the ionosphere. Although this is proper, some of the more subtle solar induced effects provide the means of propagation without using the ionosphere. It is the Sun which provides our weather, and temperature and turbulence in the atmosphere also affects propagation. The troposphere was discussed in Chapter 3, and its changes through both the Sun's effects and related seasonal activity makes it a medium capable of supporting radio wave propagation.

Early one morning in January 1946, the first signals were bounced off the Moon, and their return was detected on Earth. This was the first space communication successfully completed, although it was not the first attempted. The advent of missiles and artificial satellites brought more advances in communications with outer space. Today space communications reach out beyond the limits of our solar system. Even the ionized trails left by meteorites in the evening sky can, and are, used for communications by radio waves. We shall look at some of these more esoteric methods, although the list will not be exhaustive.

Tropospheric Propagation

Early in Chapter 3 the troposphere was described briefly, and it was noted that it can support radio wave propagation under certain circumstances. With the proper equipment, and path layout, tropospheric bending and scattering of a radio wave can provide reliable communications out to a distance of 1500 km or more. The bending mode is most common, but scatter techniques have also provided similar capabilities.

The troposphere contains about 75% of the mass of the atmosphere, and all of the moisture and dust. It is the moisture content and temperature of this air mass which are most intimately involved with tropospheric bending, or scattering, of radio waves. Because these components are most affected

75

up to about 1 km in altitude, their effects usually are most prevalent over ranges out to about 250 km. This distance can be increased however if sufficient power is available.

Air masses which make up the troposphere often move on a large scale. Meteorologists call them "weather systems" and they can retain their characteristics over long periods of time. If a large mass of air moving down from the polar regions is overrun by a mass of warm southern air, a temperature differential will exist at their boundary. This causes a *temperature inversion* to exist at one or two thousand metres in altitude.

A normal atmosphere has a steady decline of temperature as the altitude increases, as Figure 4 showed. This slow linear change in temperature will produce some refraction of the radio wave, but usually results in no more than a slow bending of the propagated wave so that the "radio" horizon is somewhat farther than the "optical" horizon. This increase is about 30% farther, and has the effect of increasing the Earth's radius by about one-third.

Although they can occur at any hour of the day, inversions occur very often at night and near, or over, water. Signal strengths decay slowly with distance, and the maximum distance which can be covered depends upon the transmitted power, aerial gain, receiving sensitivity, and local noise levels. There is, in general, no skip distance and slow fading may occur during reception due to overturning of part of the air mass along the path.

Since the frequencies involved in tropospheric propagation are in the VHF region and higher, aerial polarization is important. Horizontal polarization seems to be best for long distances, although for shorter distances just beyond LOS, vertical polarization will work about as well. If one, or both, aerials have gain and directivity then proper orientation of both is also important to maximize the received signals.

When atmospheric conditions are most favourable, a form of wave propagation known as "*ducting*" can occur. Figure 28 shows two types of temperature inversion which can occur in the low to middle atmosphere. These ducts — which one might think of as similar to a home heating duct — convey the waves between either the inversion and the Earth's surface, or between two elevated levels of similar refractive index.

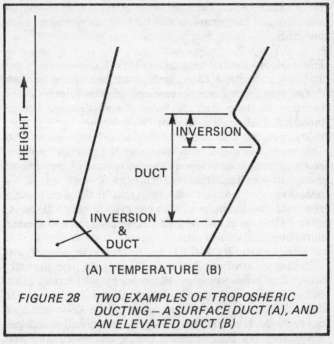

FIGURE 28   TWO EXAMPLES OF TROPOSHERIC
DUCTING – A SURFACE DUCT (A), AND
AN ELEVATED DUCT (B)

Guided propagation through ducts such as these often produce very little losses, and can extend communications over quite significant distances. Radio amateur records for this type of communications were set on VHF at a distance of 4000 km. As is usual with distances this long, the record was an all-water path from the west coast of California (USA) to the Hawaiian Islands. The dimensions of the duct can vary from as little as 6 or 7 metres in height to as much as 160 metres.

There is a low frequency cutoff below which ducting seldom occurs, and this appears to be about 50 MHz. Ducting has not been noticed at higher frequencies above 450 MHz, and this is probably due to greater absorption of the wave by water vapour. As with other forms of wave propagation, the condition and size of the medium greatly affect results to be obtained with this mode of propagation. The sharpness of the discontinuity at the boundaries of the inversion, and the humidity and temperature affect the frequencies and distances involved.

Earth–Moon–Earth Propagation (EME)

To send and receive radio signals from one of the heavenly bodies seen from Earth became one of man's dreams almost as soon as long distance radio communications became possible. EME propagation, or "*moonbounce*" as it is often called, was first discussed in a "short wave" magazine in 1930. The article was ahead of its time since the practical means of accomplishing it were beyond the capabilities of the radio art then. No one had attempted it at the time the article was published, for no one was sure that radio waves would penetrate the ionosphere. It seemed to be just a dream to most. But one young American radio amateur, and amateur astronomer, decided to act.

John DeWitt, Jr., W4ERI, had built a VHF receiver with sufficient sensitivity to hear the galactic noise from the Milky Way. This noise had been discovered by Karl Jansky of the Bell Telephone Laboratories in the United States. DeWitt decided to attempt to bounce a signal off the Moon, and see if he could hear it. In May 1940, he constructed a high-gain VHF aerial and began transmitting signals toward the Moon.

The experiment was a failure, not of implementation, but rather one of technology. It would take a larger aerial, more power, and a better receiver to do the job. But, before DeWitt could acquire the necessary equipment, World War II began for the United States. As he was of military age, DeWitt entered the US Army, and because of his talents and ability, he quickly rose in the field of military communications. By war's end, he had attained the rank of lieutenant colonel, and was in command of the US Army Evans Signal Laboratory in New Jersey.

Fate is often enigmatic, and when most of the laboratory's military work disappeared, DeWitt and his fellow scientists and engineers were available to answer a question the US Government had about the V-2 rocket attacks on London during the war. The question was "could an enemy direct a radio controlled rocket at the US?". Could radio and radar waves penetrate the ionosphere, or not? The task was given to DeWitt and his laboratory to prove one way or another.

The scientists made mathematical calculations to show they had the means to do the job, all that was left was to demonstrate it could be done. On the morning of 10 January 1946, after a month or so of testing, DeWitt and his group "fired up" the moonbounce equipment. The transmitter sent out 1-second pulses every 4 seconds. Finally, after some "tweaking" of the receiving equipment, the return pulses were heard. Man had finally touched a stellar object in space, even if only electronically.

What is required to bounce signals off the Moon? There were some formidable obstacles in 1946 which today are nothing more than routine tasks. Two major problems must be overcome. The first is that the Moon is not a large, nor efficient, reflector of radio waves. Any astronomer knows that the "*albedo*" of the Moon is only 7%. The albedo is the reflective ability of the Moon, and under the best of viewing conditions, only 7% of any incident energy is reflected by the Moon.

The Moon is just 3500 km in diameter, and its eccentric orbit carries it from 356,000 km at its closest approach to Earth, out to just over 406,000 km away. Since the power in a radio wave varies inversely with the square of the distance travelled, this means only one ten-thousand millionth of the power radiated from Earth will reach the Moon. It will suffer this same loss on the return trip. To find out if a given system will be capable of moonbounce communications, it is necessary to do a little harmless mathematical calculation. Just as one budgets expenses versus income, it is necessary to do the same with the energy involved in the two way trip to the Moon and back.

Path Losses, Power Budgets and Doppler Effects

The free-space path loss between any two points is given by the formula:

$$a = 33 + 20\log(f) + 20\log(D) ,$$

where

$$a = \text{attenuation in decibels (dB)}$$
$$f = \text{frequency in MHz, and}$$
$$D = \text{distance in kilometres.}$$

The "*decibel*" may be a new name to some readers, but it is a simple mathematical concept. (Those unfamiliar with the decibel and its use are referred to Appendix A for a more complete discussion.) For purposes of this discussion, it can be simply described as a dimensionless ratio between two numbers.

An increase in dB means an increase in the ratio of the two like quantities measured, and conversely, a decrease in the ratio means a decrease in the number of dB. For example, a tenfold increase means a 10 dB increase. Similarly a tenfold reduction in the ratio means a 10 dB decrease, or as it is usually written, −10 dB. A doubling, or halving, of the ratio corresponds to a +3 dB change or a −3 dB change respectively.

Logarithms can be added and subtracted just like ordinary numbers. An example of the use of the equation above will clarify things a bit. The average distance to the Moon from Earth is approximately 381,000 km. The round trip distance is then 762,000 km. The value of 20log(D) is then 20 times the log of 762,000 = 20(5.88) = 117.6 dB. The value of 20log(f) for 144 MHz = 20(2.16) = 43.2 dB. Putting these values in the formula gives the following result:

$$a = 33 + 43.2 + 117.6, \text{ and so}$$
$$a = 193.8 \text{ dB attenuation.}$$

This means the free-space attenuation of radio waves, at a frequency of 144 MHz, travelling to the Moon and back from Earth causes this *loss* of signal strength.

An attenuation of 193.8 dB expressed as a decimal number is 4.9 thousand millions less than the original transmitted signal. This amount of loss may seem overwhelming, and indeed it was prior to World War II. The mathematics said it was possible, only the technology of the time prevented it from occurring until 1946. But all is not hopeless, and it is surprisingly easy today to succeed in bouncing a signal off the Moon and hearing its return.

Power Budgets

Just as the household budget distributes available income against unavoidable expenses, a power budget distributes available power against unavoidable losses. If losses on the dB scale are negative, then power is a plus, or positive. A power budget is simply an accounting of all of these factors. The accounting goes as follows:

Output Power + 2(Aerial gain) − Losses = Received Signal

where

Output Power	=	Power delivered to Aerial
2(Aerial gain)	=	Twice the Aerial Gain
Losses	=	Path Loss
Received Signal	=	Signal delivered to Receiver.

The output power is the transmitter output power, minus the transmission line loss, which is delivered to the aerial terminals. The aerial gain, if any, is a plus, and is calculated twice because the gain is present not only on transmit, but on receive as well. The path loss is dependent upon the particular frequency, as has been seen, and in the present case is −193.8 dB.

To calculate now the losses which must be overcome, assume the transmitter delivers 1000 watts to the aerial. As we have seen, a factor of 10-times is equivalent to a +10 dB. Since 1000 is 10 × 10 × 10, and dB can be added, our 1000 watts equals a +30 dB. A very large, multi-element aerial for 144 MHz can have perhaps a 22 dB gain. Because this gain is available on both transmit and receive, then the *effective* aerial gain is +44 dB.

Our power budget now becomes:

$$(30 \text{ dB}) + (44 \text{ dB}) - (193.8 \text{ dB}) = -119.8 \text{ dB}$$

or, the signal strength presented to the receiver input terminals is −119.8 dB. To be sure, this is a weak signal, but again all is not hopeless. If the receiver input is a nominal 50 ohms, it is easy to calculate the received voltage and compare it with present day technology to see if this power budget is feasible. Without going through a lot of mathematics which are properly explained elsewhere, our −119.8 dB signal becomes approximately 0.25 *microvolts* (μv), or one-quarter of a millionth of a volt, at the receiver terminals.

This is not an unreasonable signal level for today's technology. With the proper receiving equipment it would allow narrowband voice signals, and certainly would accommodate Morse signals to be heard. Our solution however is essentially a perfect one. In real life, there are other losses which can contribute problems to our equations.

The Moon is not a perfectly smooth sphere since its surface is quite irregular. This causes some dispersion of the reflected signal. As with many stellar bodies, it "wobbles" as it rotates about its own axis. This causes a type of fading known as "libration" fading which further disperses the reflected signal. Due to its orbital eccentricity, it moves away, or toward, the Earth at speeds of up to 1500 km per hour. This results in a *"Doppler shift"* which returns the reflected signal at a slightly different frequency than the transmitted one.

We've all heard the Doppler shift. When a railway locomotive passes by at high speed and blows its horn, there is a noticeable shift in the tone of the horn as it passes. That is the Doppler shift within the hearing range of humans. It affects all frequencies, and in the case of the Moon, a rising Moon results in a rising frequency, and vice versa. It must be accounted for in the receiver when receiving moonbounce signals.

Although it all seems a bit complicated, in reality it is not. Today's technology can allow moonbounce to be achieved easily. It is possible to set up a receive-only station and listen to moonbounce signals. This is the first step in moonbounce communications. An easier step, and one which uses exactly the same techniques, is propagation to and from artificial satellites.

Artificial Satellite Communications
The Moon is a natural satellite of the Earth. A body which orbits another body in space is called a satellite. If that satellite is man-made, it is usually called a *"spacecraft"*.

Spacecraft can be manned, or unmanned, but the propagation of radio waves to and from the spacecraft remain the same. Only the mechanics of the problem change, with orbital time being a main obstacle.

Although the Moon has a period of about 27 days, it differs from the Sun in that the Moon remains visible for long periods of time. In other words, as the Earth revolves the Sun appears to rise and set regularly, and its hours of visibility vary with the season. The rotation of the Moon about the Earth, combined with the orbital paths of both bodies make the Moon visible for many hours at a time, regardless of the season. The Moon can be visible during night-time as well as daytime hours.

A similar situation holds for artificial satellites, or spacecraft. There is a correspondence between the altitude of a spacecraft and its orbital velocity. The lower the altitude the higher the velocity required to keep it in orbit. The higher the velocity, the less time the spacecraft will be visible from a given spot on Earth. Figure 29 shows a graphical illustration of satellite visibility versus orbital altitude.

In the figure it can be seen that low altitude spacecraft are only overhead for minutes. The maximum overhead time occurs when the "*pass*" goes through a point directly over the observer's head. This point is called the "*zenith point*". If the pass does not go through the zenith point, then the time the spacecraft is above the local horizon is less than the maximum time.

For example, with the spacecraft at an altitude of 2000 km, a zenith pass would take just over 26 minutes. The ground range of an Earth based station versus orbital altitude is given in Figure 30. This is the maximum range possible for the orbital altitude specified. The "*slant range*" from the ground observer is equal to the orbital altitude for a zenith pass. As the orbit moves away from the zenith point, the spacecraft appears to get lower and lower on the horizon, and the slant range gets longer. Hence it is above the local horizon for fewer minutes each pass.

Without going into the mathematics of this problem, if the slant range goes from 2000 km to 2500 km, then the visible time available to the ground observer is only about 17 minutes.

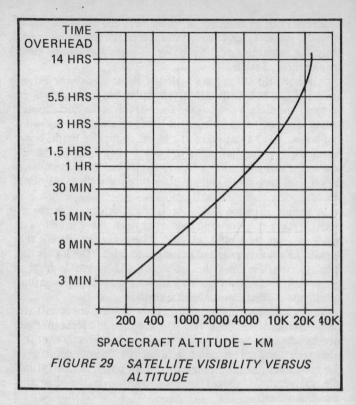

FIGURE 29 SATELLITE VISIBILITY VERSUS ALTITUDE

Finally, the precession of the orbital plane will keep the spacecraft from emerging up over the observer's horizon for a while. This means there is a circular range around the observer's location from which the spacecraft may be seen. This corresponds to the communication range from the observer's point as well.

If two ground observers wish to communicate via radio, then they must either be within the same ground range circle, or their two areas of coverage must overlap. Figure 31 shows two ground observer points with overlapping visual and radio coverage circles. Although each observer may see the spacecraft throughout the limits of their own individual coverage areas, only when the spacecraft is within LOS of both stations

84

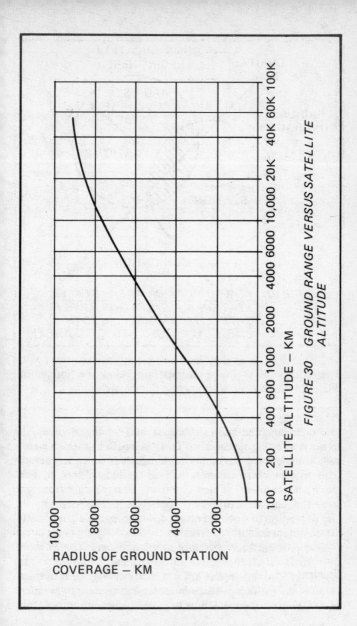

FIGURE 30 GROUND RANGE VERSUS SATELLITE ALTITUDE

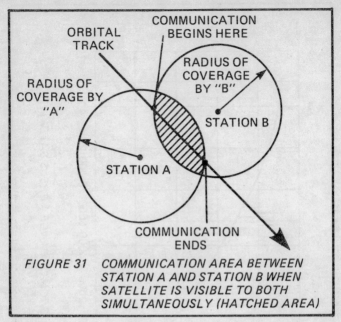

FIGURE 31   COMMUNICATION AREA BETWEEN
STATION A AND STATION B WHEN
SATELLITE IS VISIBLE TO BOTH
SIMULTANEOUSLY (HATCHED AREA)

simultaneously, may they have two-way communications with
each other. When the spacecraft falls below the horizon of
one of them, communications stop immediately.

Power Budgets Et Al
The same equation and calculations used for the Moon apply
to lower orbiting spacecraft. There is a path loss which varies
with distance and frequency, although it is much less severe
than with extreme distances such as the lunar distance. The
requirements for aerial gain and transmitter power output are
somewhat eased because the distance is less. This means much
less sophisticated equipment is needed to provide good satellite communications.

One problem becomes more severe however. The Doppler
shift for lower altitude spacecraft is greater, due mainly to the
higher velocity required at lower orbital altitudes. The average
Doppler shift at moonrise, or moonset, can amount to as much
as ±4000 Hz. As the Moon becomes higher in the sky, this

value drops to zero at some point, since the *change* in slant range to the Moon has dropped to zero as well. The effect is one of a slowly varying tone which starts high in frequency, slowly drops through "zero beat", then continues on to the other extreme.

The amount of Doppler shift is proportional to the frequency involved, getting higher as the frequency increases. At 100 MHz for example, the Doppler shift for a spacecraft at 2000 km altitude is about ±5000 Hz. At 400 MHz this value rises to about ±23.5 kHz for the same altitude. Any receiving equipment must be able to compensate for this shift, either automatically, or by manual tuning.

Polarization of the aerial is sometimes important since different spacecraft may carry different types of aerials themselves. In addition, some spacecraft are not stabilised in orbit, and may tumble in random fashion. Normally circular polarization will account for all of these cases. The only drawback is that the ground based circularly polarized aerial must have about 3 dB gain (2 times) when used against a linearly polarized spacecraft aerial.

Meteorite Propagation

Although radio wave propagation by way of the ionized trails left by meteors entering the Earth's atmosphere is a rather esoteric means of communications, it is nevertheless being pursued by several experimenters as an alternative means of providing communications. Much work remains to be done, however recent developments have shown progress in the field of meteorite propagation.

More properly known as meteorite "scatter" propagation, it uses the ionized trail left by meteorites as they enter and burn in the atmosphere. Often referred to as "shooting stars" in reality they are not stars. They are a form of *"space debris"*, and indeed, their name comes from the Greek "meteora" which means "things in the air". They can vary from the size of a speck of dust, to quite large meteors such as the one which fell in Arizona, USA. This large meteor left a hole over 180 metres deep and 1.5 km wide. Many are smaller however, often about the size of a football, and are consumed upon entering the atmosphere.

Meteors are constantly entering the atmosphere, beginning in early January with the Quadrantids, and continuing on through December with the Geminids and the Ursids. They are named for their apparent point of origin in various constellations, stars, or comets. Some are considered to be "major" showers and many occur during daytime hours.

The meteors which enter the atmosphere may be composed of metals or minerals, but all begin to ionize at an altitude comparable to the E layer. The heat of friction causes the ionization to form as a dense cylinder behind the meteor, some of which is visible to the naked eye. The number and duration of these trails is greater with the major showers, although some of the lesser showers have produced scattered usable signals.

The user of meteor scatter propagation is limited to the frequency range of about 50 MHz and up. The distances involved range from about 2000 km at 50 MHz, up to just a few hundred kilometres at 144 MHz. If a major shower is in progress, it is possible to have bursts of one or two minutes where continuous propagation is possible. It is not necessary however to wait for one of these instances to successfully propagate signals by way of meteor scatter.

The variability of meteorite propagation should not cause concern since proper operational procedures can give good results. Early on in meteor scatter experiments, high speed Morse code was used, and the transmissions were on accurately known frequencies and times. One typical arrangement was for one station to transmit "on the minute" for 15 seconds, and then standby. The second station would transmit on the half-minute for 15 seconds, and then standby. Such techniques often exchanged adequate information in bursts of a few seconds each.

Voice contacts followed Morse contacts, and with the advent of single-sideband (SSB) transmission, it has become even more successful.

Chapter 6

NOISE

Noise has been defined in the past as any unwanted signal, or interference, which degrades reception of the desired signal. While this definition is all-encompassing, it is flawed because of its sweeping generality. Unwanted signals, or interference, may be quite coherent however undesirable they may be. It may be possible to make good sense of the desired signal even in their presence. Noise, in this book, is considered to be what most listeners call "*static*".

The main characteristic of noise, or static, is that it is either random, impulsive, or both in nature. Random noise, or fluctuation noise as it is sometimes called, consists of a large number of noise pulses which are not related in any equal time sequence. Types of random noise include thermally generated noise, static "crashes", and noise which arrives from interstellar space (cosmic noise).

Impulse noise consists of discrete, well separated noise pulses which do have a detectable time sequence between them. Typical types of impulse noise are those made by generator brush noise, ignition noise, and thermostat noise. A new source of this type of noise has come about through the personal computer. Computers have one or more "*time bases*" on which they depend for proper operation. Without proper shielding and suppression techniques, these noise pulses are easily radiated directly, or through the mains wiring.

Atmospheric Noise

It has been estimated that there are between 1500 and 2000 thunderstorms in action worldwide at any given moment. It has also been estimated that there are at least 100 lightning strikes per second as a result of these storms. Lightning strikes have been estimated to carry currents of from 20,000 amperes up to 1,000,000 amperes or more. These strikes produce a type of radiation known as "*damped oscillations*". A damped oscillation is one which starts out with high intensity and drops off gradually until it falls to zero.

The initial sharpness of the thunderclap following a lightning strike, followed by the dull rumble as the sound fades is an aural indication of a damped oscillation. Because a lightning strike is an electromagnetic event, it too follows propagation laws. With the exception of *"precipitation static"*, thunderstorm activity and its associated lightning account for the majority of noise heard in receivers.

Because thunderstorm activity is seasonal, as well as geographical, it can be expected to vary. While there is no direct correlation established as yet, scientists over the years have found increases in tropical storm and hurricane activity in certain geographical areas which correspond with increased sunspot activity. Snowfall has been found to be higher, and icebergs more numerous, with increasing sunspot numbers.

Weather is a highly complex phenomenon, but there are indications that global weather follows certain wavelike movements in the atmosphere. The change from low sunspot activity to high sunspot activity causes known barometric pressure shifts from low latitudes to high latitudes and back again. It is the low latitudes which experience the greatest thunderstorm activity. In these latitudes, there appears to be a shifting of the storm activity laterally along the Equator as well.

Nevertheless, the electromagnetic noise from these storms is propagated worldwide, and makes up most of the static heard on radio receivers. The noise level at any given location is made up of contributions by this worldwide noise plus any local activity. Quite often thunderstorm activity is greater over water, due to the greater availability of moisture.

Because the noise generated by thunderstorm activity is propagated just as any other radio wave is propagated, it is susceptible to being absorbed as well. Measurements have shown that the noise level is greater at night in the $1 - 5$ MHz region, than during the day. This is due to D layer absorption. At the higher frequencies, from 10 or 15 MHz up, there is only a little variation between night and day. The absorption is still effective during the daytime, but these higher frequencies are supported more effectively by the ionosphere.

The other major contributor to atmospheric noise is precipitation static. Precipitation static arises from particles such as dust, snow, and rain striking aerials and leaving an exchange of random energy as a result of the impact. The particles often have picked up a charge due to wind, or simply falling from 1000 metres or more, and when they strike an aerial there is a discharge of this energy. These are special conditions, to be sure, but can be the major source of noise at times.

Man-made Noise

The amount of noise generated by man-made devices can be tremendous. Noise is generated anywhere an electrical connection is made or broken. Many of them are domestic appliances, or equipment in the workplace, used on a common everyday basis. They include such things as high voltage mains, light switches, vacuum cleaners, motors, petrol engines, trolleys, electric shavers, neon signs, just to name a few. The personal computer deserves mention all by itself since it generates a type of noise called "*hash*".

The computer normally uses a central clock which provides all of the timing needed for the computer to operate properly. This central clock is also divided down any number of times in order to synchronize the operation of the internal circuits so the desired events occur at the proper time. This means that all of these frequencies can be radiated directly through the atmosphere, or through the mains, if not properly shielded and filtered.

Noise is predominantly vertically polarized, particularly man-made noise. Unless it is necessary to match the polarization of the transmitting station, horizontal polarization of the receiving aerial will give a substantial reduction of noise in most cases. In the case where a broadcast station uses vertical polarization, the amount of power radiated by its aerial is usually high enough so that polarization is not of consequence. Television and FM broadcasting aerials are horizontally polarized for their greater noise protection.

Cosmic Noise

Measurements have shown that considerable noise originates outside of our atmosphere. The Sun is, of course, a superb noise source, but it is not the only one in interstellar space.

The effects of cosmic noise are most noticed above 15 MHz. The principal source of cosmic noise for Earth is our own galaxy — the Milky Way.

Our galaxy is similar to many others in the Universe and it resembles a flat spiral shape. If the Earth's poles and Equator are projected out onto a *"celestial sphere"* which includes our Milky Way, it would resemble the simple diagram shown in Figure 32. Star positions are determined from Earth by

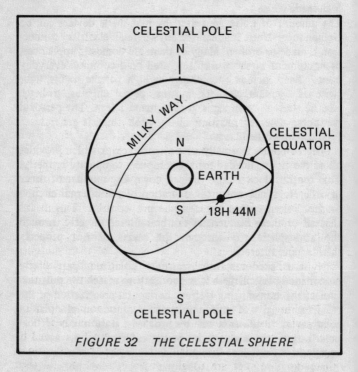

FIGURE 32   THE CELESTIAL SPHERE

angular coordinates measured from a reference point on the celestial sphere in a manner similar to longitude and latitude.

The projection of the Earth's Equator on the celestial sphere is called the *"celestial equator"*, and the projection of the poles on the celestial sphere are called the *"celestial poles"*. Astronomers assign star positions by giving the *"right ascension*", in hours, and the "*declination*" in degrees above or below the celestial equator. In the figure, the position of the Milky Way is shown with respect to the celestial equator.

The right ascension is the celestial longitude measured eastward on the celestial equator from a point where the Sun crosses the celestial equator in the spring, or vernal equinox. The declination is simply measured north or south from the celestial equator and has values from 0 to ±90 degrees respectively.

A number of scientists have located the greatest source of cosmic noise at a point having a right ascension of 18 hours, and a declination of about −30 degrees. There are other isolated noise sources both in the plane of the Milky Way, and elsewhere, but this is the greatest noise source discovered so far. The greatest amount of this cosmic noise occurs when the portion of the sky over the receiving station is at this point.

Cosmic noise has the same characteristics as fluctuation noise. That is, it occurs with distinct regularity. A typical example is the noise emanating from the planet Jupiter. It may be heard over a broad frequency range, centred roughly on 21 MHz. It requires no special receiving equipment or aerials. It is a pulsing sound, and is easily recognizable. Indeed, the word "*pulsar*" is a contraction of the words "pulsing star", of which there are many in the celestial sky. These pulsars are usually stars at the end of their lifetimes. They are neutron stars which are rotating rapidly and emit streams of particulate matter, and other radiations from their polar regions.

The intensity of cosmic noise varies considerably depending upon where one looks at the galaxy. Because these noise sources are essentially point sources they can be avoided by proper positioning of the aerial. For satellite communications, these noise sources are usually noted in advance, and their effects avoided where possible. Many observatories, such as the Royal Astronomical Observatory, make "sky maps" showing the background radiation of the sky noise for various frequencies.

Considerable research is continuing into cosmic radiation and noise. This research is aimed at determining its variation

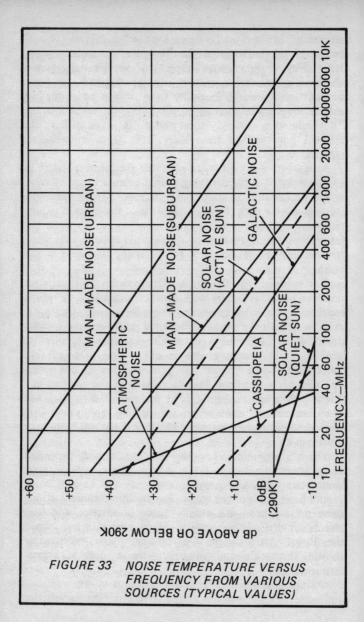

FIGURE 33   NOISE TEMPERATURE VERSUS FREQUENCY FROM VARIOUS SOURCES (TYPICAL VALUES)

94

with time of day, season, geographical location, frequency, and receiving aerial directivity. For most sky wave propagation needs, cosmic noise is not a great factor since it is absorbed at low frequencies, and it only need be taken into account at frequencies above 15 MHz. Figure 33 shows how the various types of noise vary with frequency.

Receiver Noise

All molecular motion ceases at −273.1 degrees Celsius, or absolute zero temperature. This temperature is also known as 0 kelvin (K), named after the British physicist and mathematician William Thompson, the 1st Baron Kelvin. Since temperature is a measure of molecular activity, the greater the temperature, the greater the activity. But temperature is also a measure of heat, and heat can cause noise.

Thermal noise occurs in any conductor with an electric current flowing in it. If this conductor is a receiving aerial, then the noise generated is known as "*aerial noise*". If the receiver to which this aerial is connected generated no noise of its own, then the aerial noise would determine the weakest signal which could be received. Unfortunately, since no receiver is noiseless, the aerial noise only adds to that generated by the receiver.

To readily quantify how much noise is contributed by the various components of a receiving system, a "*noise temperature*" concept has been developed, and is measured in kelvin. In this fashion, equivalent values for resistances, tuned circuits, semiconductors and valves used in receivers can be characterized with a common measuring standard. Normally, something called "*room ambient*" is the nominal reference point, and is set at 290 kelvin by convention.

At low, medium and high frequencies, atmospheric and man-made noise combine to be considerably greater than 290 kelvin. Therefore, it is not necessary to have a very sensitive receiver since the external noise will set the level of the weakest signal which can be heard. Such is not the case at VHF and above, particularly in space communications.

95

A survey done by the Royal Astronomical Observatory of the cosmic noise received at a frequency of 400 MHz showed a background sky temperature of 100 kelvin. In this case the receiving aerial, its feedline, and the early stages in the receiver proper should contribute much less noise than this if very weak signals are anticipated.

Some Final Thoughts

At this point we are at the close of a story which has no end. Future discoveries in the arena of electromagnetic propagation will continue to add to the wealth of knowledge already recorded. The radio spectrum is an indestructible resource for all practical purposes, and provides mankind with abilities and applications the ancients rarely dreamed of.

Some aspects of radio wave propagation have only been touched upon lightly, while some of the more esoteric have only been suggested. The whole subject of noise can cover a vast number of pages, far more than were presented here. Interstellar propagation is another subject which has merely been hinted at here. But if this book has stimulated a few readers to delve deeper into a very interesting field then its mission has been a success.

Appendix A

LOGARITHMS AND DECIBELS

The 16th century produced a number of excellent mathematicians in Europe. John Napier, Baron of Merchiston, was one of them, for it was Napier who discovered logarithms. He had been enrolled at St. Andrews where he studied mathematics and theology, but his mind turned more and more toward mathematics. Many of his writings exist today, and on one of his pages the following table appears:

—	I	II	III	IIII	V....
1	2	4	8	16	32 ....

Napier noticed that the top row was an *"arithmetic progression"*, that is each number is one greater than the previous number. He saw that the lower row of numbers was a *"geometrical progression"*, that is each number is greater by a larger amount than the previous one.

The lower row is in fact a binary series — that is each number is a *"power"* of 2. A power of a number is the number of times it is multiplied by itself. By convention, "1" is 2 not raised to any power, hence the (—). In the top row, "I" indicates 2 alone, "II" indicates $2 \times 2 = 4$, etc. Yet both progressions grow together, for every number in the top row has a corresponding number in the lower row. Similarly, for every number in the lower row, there is a corresponding one in the top row.

Napier called the type of number in the top row the *"logarithm"* of the number in the bottom row. Knowing it, the number in the lower row — the *"antilogarithm"* — can be determined and vice versa. But the binary system of numbers is only used in the world of mathematics and computing systems. The decimal system — based on the numbers 0 through 9 — is the one most used worldwide. Napier began his calculations of logarithms based on the decimal system, or what mathematicians call "the base 10".

It took 25 years for Napier to finish his calculations, but they were eagerly accepted by such names as Johannes Kepler, and Tycho Brahe when they were published. Both Kepler and Brahe were astronomers, and worked with large numbers associated with the mass of planets, and their distances, to name just two. Napier's logarithms brought a simplification to astronomy since his logarithms could be simply added, and the antilog determined to get the final result. Logarithms substitute the simpler mathematical function "addition" for the more complicated function of "multiplication".

For example, from the table above everyone knows that $4 \times 8 = 32$, but by adding the logarithms instead, one sees that II + III = V, and 2 raised to the "V" (or 5th) power also equals 32. So addition in logarithms equals multiplication in the mathematical base number. For base 2 mathematical systems the problem is trivial, but for other bases such as the decimal system it is not. For example, 2 in a decimal system has a logarithm of 0.30103. In other words, 10 raised to the 0.30103 power equals 2. Napier calculated his logarithms out to seven figures — no wonder it took 25 years.

Hearing and Sound Levels

All human senses have a threshold below which we detect nothing. Seeing, for example, has a threshold which can be demonstrated by looking at the stars on a clear night. There is a level below which fainter stars cannot be perceived by the human eye, even though a telescope shows them to be there. Astronomers call these "magnitude 6" stars, with magnitude 1 stars being the brightest. The important thing is that there is a sharp cutoff of visibility at magnitude 6 where our eyes are concerned.

The same is true of our hearing. If one were to listen to a sustained note on a musical instrument while walking away from it, the sound level does not decrease in a linear fashion. That is, it doesn't get weaker and weaker as we walk away, yet remain audible no matter how far we travel. Instead the sound diminishes for a while, then suddenly drops below our threshold of hearing, and nothing further is heard. The smallest sound heard before vanishing is the threshold of our hearing.

When scientists began to measure sound intensities and took this phenomena into account, they named a ten-fold change in sound level the "*bel*" after the inventor of the telephone Alexander Graham Bell. It turned out that this level of change was too high to be of much use, and so they settled upon 1/10th of the amount — the "*decibel*". Since human hearing was not linear, but responded to very faint sounds as well as tolerating very loud sounds, here was an ideal application of Napier's logarithms.

If the intensity of sound at the threshold is taken as 0 decibels (dB), then the table below shows the progression of both sound energy levels and decibels:

1 unit of sound energy	=	0 dB
1.26 units of sound energy	=	1 dB
1.58 " " " "	=	2 dB
2 " " " "	=	3 dB
4 " " " "	=	6 dB
8 " " " "	=	9 dB
10 " " " "	=	10 dB
100 " " " "	=	20 dB
1000 " " " "	=	30 dB, and so on.

Several things are apparent from the table. First an increase by a factor of 2 is equivalent to adding 3 dB. Similarly, a decrease of two — a factor of ½ — results in a lessening of 3 dB. A factor of 10 times is equal to a 10 dB increase, and since $10 \times 10 = 100$, then a 100 times increase equals 10 dB *plus* an additional 10 dB or a total of 20 dB.

The decibel is then a comparison of two different sound levels as originally conceived. It does not have to be limited to sound however. Any ratio of equal or like quantities can be compared in this fashion. For this comparison, the formula is:

$$dB = 10\log(P1/P2) ,$$

where P1 = first level, and P2 = second level.

If P1 is twice the level of P2, then the formula becomes:

$$dB = 10\log(2)$$

$$= 10(0.30103)$$

$$dB = 3.0103 \ .$$

The decimal portion is equally ignored so the dB change for a ratio of 2 is 3 dB as the previous table showed.

Decibels are added for multiplication, and are subtracted for division. In power budget calculations, such as shown in Chapter 5, a loss in dB is given a minus sign. In this fashion, transmitter output power, and aerial gain are positive, and space loss is negative. By converting these components of a power budget to dB, simple addition and subtraction can make manipulation of the required values easy to see.

Appendix B

GLOSSARY

Absorption
Decrease in energy due to losses suffered by the radio wave to Earth and to the ions of the ionosphere.

Alternating Current
Electrical current which reverses direction at regularly recurring intervals.

Amplitude
The maximum value of alternating current or voltage.

Angle of Incidence
The angle between the perpendicular to a reflecting surface and an incident wave at the point it strikes the surface. A wave perpendicular to a surface has a zero angle of incidence.

Angle of Refraction
The angle between the perpendicular to a surface separating two different media and the direction to which the radio waves go when entering the second medium.

Aerial
A device for sending radio waves into space, or for receiving them.

Aerial Array
An aerial consisting of several elemental aerials or conductors.

Aerial Gain
The power per unit area in the required direction to the average power per unit area. Aerial gain measures the directivity of an aerial to a non-directional aerial.

Atmospheric Noise
Noise or static that is due to natural causes. It is due mainly to thunderstorm activity.

Attenuation

The decrease of amplitude due to losses.

Auroral Absorption

Absorption of radio waves due to auroral activity. Auroral activity is caused mainly by particle activity from the Sun.

Blackout

The interruption of radio communications due to excessive absorption caused by solar flares. During severe blackouts, all frequencies above 1500 kHz are absorbed excessively in the daylight zone.

Collision Frequency

The number of collisions between an electron and a molecule of a gas per unit time. It is dependent upon the velocity of the electron and the mean free path between molecules.

Conductivity

The reciprocal of resistivity.

Cosmic Noise

Radio static whose origin is outside the Earth and its atmosphere. The source may be sunspots, stars, or of extragalactic origin.

Critical Frequency

The maximum frequency an ionospheric layer will reflect at vertical incidence.

D Layer

The lowest regular ionospheric layer. It primarily absorbs sky-waves, and normally does not reflect them.

Decibel

A standard unit of power ratio. It is equal to ten times the logarithm (to the base 10) for the ratio of two powers.

Dielectric Constant

The ratio between the specific inductive capacity of a material and that of a vacuum. Dielectrics, such as mica, increase the value of capacitors.

Diffraction
Bending of electromagnetic waves around obstacles.

Direct Wave
The wave that travels directly between a transmitting aerial and a receiving aerial without reflections.

E Layer
A regular ionospheric layer with an average height of about 100 km. Its ionization is dependent upon the Sun's angle, and disappears at night.

Ecliptic
The annual path of the Earth around the Sun.

Electrical Interference
Noise generated by electrical apparatus other than radio stations.

Electromagnetic Wave
A radio wave which is a transverse wave travelling with the velocity of light.

F1 Layer
A regular ionospheric layer occurring at an average height of 225 km during daylight hours.

F2 Layer
The uppermost, most highly ionized, layer occurring throughout 24 hours. Its height varies from 225 km during night-time, to at least 300 km at midday. It is the primary mode for long-distance communication by radio.

Galaxy
A system containing numerous stars, such as the Milky Way.

Ground Reflected Wave
That portion of a ground wave which is reflected off the ground (Earth).

Ground Wave
A wave propagated solely over earth, and does not use the ionosphere for propagation.

Heaviside Layer
Original name for the ionosphere. Sometimes limited to the E layer only.

HF Band
The frequency range of from 3.0 to 30.0 megahertz.

Hop
Travel of a radio wave from the transmitting aerial up to the ionosphere and back to Earth. The number of hops is the number of times the ionosphere reflects the wave.

Horizontal Polarization
A linearly polarized wave whose electric field is parallel to the Earth.

Impulse Noise
Noise due to abrupt changes, usually of short duration.

Ion
A positively, or negatively, charged particle such as an electron, or a proton.

Ionization
The process of producing ions.

Ionosphere
The collection of ionized layers occurring in the upper atmosphere of the Earth, above 50 km.

Ionospheric Storms
Periods of abnormal ionization, usually caused by abnormal particulate radiation from the Sun. Accompanied by excessive absorption, abnormal virtual heights and abnormal critical frequencies.

KM
Kilometre (km).

Kilohertz (kHz)
1000 hertz (cycles-per-second).

Latitude
The angular distance, north or south, from the Earth's Equator.

Linearly Polarized Wave
A transverse electromagnetic wave which has a constant direction for its electric and magnetic fields.

Line Of Sight (LOS)
Visual distance to the horizon from an elevated point, including any atmospheric refraction.

Longitude
The angular distance, east or west, from the Greenwich meridian. The Greenwich meridian is universally considered to be zero degrees longitude.

Lowest Useful Frequency
The lower limiting high-frequency for satisfactory sky-wave propagation. It is primarily determined by equipment, aerials, local noise levels, and path absorption.

Magnetic Storm
Occur concurrently with ionospheric storms, and are the result of intense particle radiation from the Sun.

Maximum Usable Frequency
The highest usable frequency for satisfactory communications over a given sky-wave propagation path. It is directly related to the critical frequency.

MF Band
The Medium Frequency band extends from 300 kHz to 3.0 MHz.

MHz
Megahertz, or 1,000,000 hertz (cycles-per-second).

Noise

Interference whose energy is distributed over a very wide frequency range.

Noise Figure

A term used to rate how much excess noise is contributed to the received signal by the receiver itself.

Omnidirectional Aerial

An isotropic radiator, or aerial, which radiates energy uniformly in all directions. Such an aerial does not exist but is used as a reference.

Optimum Traffic Frequency (FOT)

A frequency chosen to be 85% of the MUF to provide a stable frequency, free of ionospheric fluctuations, on a day-to-day basis.

Photosphere

The visible disk of the Sun.

Precipitation Static

Noise, or static, experienced during dust storms, rainstorms, and snow storms. Often caused by the impact of the particulate matter against the aerial. Can also be caused by coronal discharges.

Radio Wave Propagation

The transfer of electromagnetic energy at radio frequencies.

Random Noise

Noise due to a large number of sources, and is variable in time.

Ray Path

A straight geometric path between any two points such as a transmitting aerial and a receiving aerial.

Reflected Wave

Reflection of an incident wave back into the first medium when it strikes the boundary between two different media.

Refracted Wave
A radio wave travelling from one medium to another which is not reflected, but is caused to follow a curved path in the second medium.

Right Ascension
Celestial longitude measured in hours eastward from the point where the Earth's orbit crosses the celestial equator (the Vernal Equinox).

Short Wave
Radio frequencies in the range from 1.5 to 30.0 MHz, and used for sky-wave propagation.

SID
Sudden ionospheric disturbance.

Skip Distance
Minimum distance at which a specific frequency wave can be returned to Earth by reflection off the ionosphere.

Sky-wave
A radio wave radiated in a skyward direction and received after being reflected off the ionosphere.

Sporadic-E (Es)
Intermittent ionization which appears at the same height as the E layer. Occurs at all hours of the day, and is more noticeable in polar regions.

Static
All forms of radio noise.

Sudden Ionospheric Disturbance (SID)
Sudden increase in the lower layers of the ionosphere. Normally associated with bright solar eruptions, or flares. Onset occurs in minutes, but effects last for hours or days.

Sunspots
Areas of solar activity on the surface of the Sun, and are

sources of magnetic, and ultraviolet radiation. Visible to the naked eye when suitable precautions are taken to prevent eye injury when viewing the Sun.

Sunspot Cycle

An average of 11 years from one maximum to another in sunspot activity.

Sunspot Number (SSN)

An index of solar activity, and is expressed as a constant multiplied by 10 times the number sunspot groups plus individual spots. See Wolf's number.

SHF Band

Superhigh frequencies ranging from 3,000 to 30,000 MHz.

Thermal Noise

Noise generated in conductors due to thermal motions induced by electrons in the conductor.

Transverse Wave

A wave in which the electric and magnetic fields are transverse to the direction of propagation.

Troposphere

The lower portion of the Earth's atmosphere up to an average height of 11 km. Temperatures normally decrease linearly with altitude in the troposphere.

UHF Band

The ultra-high frequencies which range from 300 to 3,000 MHz.

Ultraviolet

Electromagnetic radiation at frequencies above visible light.

Vertically Polarized Wave

An electromagnetic wave whose electric field is perpendicular to the Earth's surface.

VHF Band

The very-high frequency range which goes from 30.0 to 300 MHz.

Virtual Height

The height of an equivalent reflection point which causes a radio wave to travel to the ionosphere and back, *in the same time* as required for an actual reflection.

Wave

Disturbance propagated through a medium, a period variation, or its graphical representation.

Wavelength

The distance in metres travelled by a wave over the time interval for one cycle to be completed. It is equal to the velocity of the wave divided by its frequency.

Wolf's Number

The formula is $R = k(10g + f)$, and provides a measure of sunspot activity consistent with various observations. The constant, k, varies with the individual observer and his equipment.

Index

A

Absorption, 22, 25, 27, 31-35, 44, 45, 50, 52, 54, 57, 65, 67, 77
Angle of Arrival, 23
Appleton, Sir Edward V., 23, 25
Atmosphere, 10, 19, 21, 22, 23, 25-34, 37, 39, 58, 75, 76, 87, 88
Auroral, 8, 19, 27, 33, 35, 52

B

Breit, G., 23

C

Carbon-14, 18
Celestial,
   Sphere, 92
   Equator, 92-95
   Poles, 92

D

D layer, 25, 27, 34
Decibel, 80
Diurnal, 12, 25, 49, 50
Doppler Shift, 79, 82, 86, 87
Douglass, Prof. A. E., 16
Ducting, 76, 77

E

E layer, 23, 25, 27, 28, 29, 35
Eclipse, 5, 23
Electrons, 5, 12, 23, 24, 32, 44, 45
EME, 78

F

F1 layer, 28, 29
F2 layer, 28-31
Flares, 7, 13, 25, 32, 52
FOT, 50

G

Galileo, 9
Grey Line, 58-65
Ground-wave, 47, 65-73

H

Hale, Dr G. E., 10, 11
Hash, 91
Heaviside, Sir Oliver, 22
Height, layer, 23, 41, 43, 47

Height, tropopause, 21
Hertz, Heinrich, 22
Hurricanes, 10, 11, 21

I

Ionosphere, 20, 23-35, 75
Ionospheric storms, 32, 52
Inversions, 76-78
Impulse noise, 89

K

Kelvin, Lord, 95
Kennelly, Arthur, 22

L

Layers,
   Ozone, 22
   Sporadic-E, 27
   Tropopause, 21
   Warm, 22
Logarithms, 80
LUF, Lowest Usable Frequency, 50, 53, 67

M

Maunder, Prof. E. W., 17
Maunder Minimum, 15, 17, 18
Meteor theory, 2
Meteorites, 13, 75, 87
Moonbounce (EME), 78, 79
MUF, Maximum Usable Frequency, 47-57, 60
Multi-hop, 39, 67
Multi-path (1-Hop, 2-Hop), 39, 40, 49, 53, 55

N

Noise,
   Atmospheric, 89-91
   Cosmic, 89, 91-96
   Impulse, 89
   Man-made, 91
   Random, 89, 90
   Sky, 95
   Static, 89-91
   Temperature, 95

P

Particulate matter, 5, 19, 32, 34
Pedersen Ray, 42, 49
Perihelion, 15

111

P (contd.)
Polarity
    Electrical/Magnetic, 13
    Sunspots, 13
Power Budgets, 79, 81, 82, 86

R
Radiation, 3, 4, 5, 7, 19-25, 42,
    45-49, 68
Radio Wave, 37-47, 54, 57, 67

S
Satellite, 71, 73, 83
Seasonal changes, 12, 15
Schwabe, Hendrik, 13
Sky-wave, 39-47, 64, 67, 72
SID, Sudden Ionospheric
    Disturbance, 32-35
Solar,
    Activity, 14, 15, 18, 57
    Energy, 2, 3
    Equator, 11
    Month, 11
    Observatory, 14

    Wind, 5, 19
Sporadic-E, 27, 49, 56, 57
Sun,
    Layers, 10
Sunspots, 3, 8-17

T
Temperature,
    Noise, 95
    Sky, 96
Thompson, W., 95
Trans-Equatorial (TE), 57, 58
Tree Rings, 16-18
Tuve, M. A., 23

U
Ultra-violet, 8

W
Weather, 15
Wolf, (Wolfs Number), 14,15

Z
Zurich (Observatory), 14, 15

Please note following is a list of other titles that are available in our range of Radio, Electronics and Computer books.

These should be available from all good Booksellers, Radio Component Dealers and Mail Order Companies.

However, should you experience difficulty in obtaining any title in your area, then please write directly to the Publisher enclosing payment to cover the cost of the book plus adequate postage.

If you would like a complete catalogue of our entire range of Radio, Electronics and Computer Books then please send a Stamped Addressed Envelope to:

BERNARD BABANI (publishing) LTD
THE GRAMPIANS
SHEPHERDS BUSH ROAD
LONDON W6 7NF
ENGLAND

160	Coil Design and Construction Manual	£2.50
205	Hi-Fi Loudspeaker Enclosures	£2.95
208	Practical Stereo & Quadrophony Handbook	£0.75
214	Audio Enthusiast's Handbook	£0.85
219	Solid State Novelty Projects	£0.85
220	Build Your Own Solid State Hi-Fi and Audio Accessories	£0.85
222	Solid State Short Wave Receivers for Beginners	£1.95
225	A Practical Introduction to Digital ICs	£2.50
226	How to Build Advanced Short Wave Receivers	£2.95
227	Beginners Guide to Building Electronic Projects	£1.95
228	Essential Theory for the Electronics Hobbyist	£2.50
BP2	Handbook of Radio, TV, Industrial and Transmitting Tube and Valve Equivalents	£0.60
BP6	Engineer's & Machinist's Reference Tables	£1.25
BP7	Radio & Electronic Colour Codes Data Chart	£0.95
BP27	Chart of Radio, Electronic, Semiconductor and Logic Symbols	£0.95
BP28	Resistor Selection Handbook	£0.60
BP29	Major Solid State Audio Hi-Fi Construction Projects	£0.85
BP33	Electronic Calculator Users Handbook	£1.50
BP36	50 Circuits Using Germanium Silicon and Zener Diodes	£1.50
BP37	50 Projects Using Relays, SCRs and TRIACs	£2.95
BP39	50 (FET) Field Effect Transistor Projects	£2.95
BP42	50 Simple LED Circuits	£1.95
BP44	IC 555 Projects	£2.95
BP45	Projects in Opto-Electronics	£1.95
BP48	Electronic Projects for Beginners	£1.95
BP49	Popular Electronic Projects	£2.50
BP53	Practical Electronics Calculations and Formulae	£3.95
BP54	Your Electronic Calculator & Your Money	£1.35
BP56	Electronic Security Devices	£2.50
BP58	50 Circuits Using 7400 Series IC's	£2.50
BP62	The Simple Electronic Circuit & Components (Elements of Electronics — Book 1)	£3.50
BP63	Alternating Current Theory (Elements of Electronics — Book 2)	£3.50
BP64	Semiconductor Technology (Elements of Electronics — Book 3)	£3.50
BP66	Beginners Guide to Microprocessors and Computing	£1.95
BP68	Choosing and Using Your Hi-Fi	£1.65
BP69	Electronic Games	£1.75
BP70	Transistor Radio Fault-finding Chart	£0.95
BP72	A Microprocessor Primer	£1.75
BP74	Electronic Music Projects	£2.50
BP76	Power Supply Projects	£2.50
BP77	Microprocessing Systems and Circuits (Elements of Electronics — Book 4)	£2.95
BP78	Practical Computer Experiments	£1.75
BP80	Popular Electronic Circuits - Book 1	£2.95
BP84	Digital IC Projects	£1.95
BP85	International Transistor Equivalents Guide	£3.50
BP86	An Introduction to BASIC Programming Techniques	£1.95
BP87	50 Simple LED Circuits — Book 2	£1.35
BP88	How to Use Op-Amps	£2.95
BP89	Communication (Elements of Electronics — Book 5)	£2.95
BP90	Audio Projects	£2.50
BP91	An Introduction to Radio DXing	£1.95
BP92	Electronics Simplified — Crystal Set Construction	£1.75
BP93	Electronic Timer Projects	£1.95
BP94	Electronic Projects for Cars and Boats	£1.95
BP95	Model Railway Projects	£1.95
BP97	IC Projects for Beginners	£1.95
BP98	Popular Electronic Circuits — Book 2	£2.25
BP99	Mini-matrix Board Projects	£2.50
BP101	How to Identify Unmarked ICs	£0.95
BP103	Multi-circuit Board Projects	£1.95
BP104	Electronic Science Projects	£2.95
BP105	Aerial Projects	£1.95
BP106	Modern Op-amp Projects	£1.95
BP107	30 Solderless Breadboard Projects — Book 1	£2.25
BP108	International Diode Equivalents Guide	£2.25
BP109	The Art of Programming the 1K ZX81	£1.95
BP110	How to Get Your Electronic Projects Working	£2.50
BP111	Audio (Elements of Electronics — Book 6)	£3.50
BP112	A Z-80 Workshop Manual	£3.50
BP113	30 Solderless Breadboard Projects — Book 2	£2.25
BP114	The Art of Programming the 16K ZX81	£2.50
BP115	The Pre-computer Book	£1.95
BP117	Practical Electronic Building Blocks — Book 1	£1.95
BP118	Practical Electronic Building Blocks — Book 2	£1.95
BP119	The Art of Programming the ZX Spectrum	£2.50
BP120	Audio Amplifier Fault-finding Chart	£0.95
BP121	How to Design and Make Your Own PCB's	£2.50
BP122	Audio Amplifier Construction	£2.25
BP123	A Practical Introduction to Microprocessors	£2.50
BP124	Easy Add-on Projects for Spectrum, ZX81 & Ace	£2.75
BP125	25 Simple Amateur Band Aerials	£1.95
BP126	BASIC & PASCAL in Parallel	£1.50
BP127	How to Design Electronic Projects	£2.25
BP128	20 Programs for the ZX Spectrum and 16K ZX81	£1.95
BP129	An Introduction to Programming the ORIC-1	£1.95
BP130	Micro Interfacing Circuits — Book 1	£2.25
BP131	Micro Interfacing Circuits — Book 2	£2.75

BP132	25 Simple Shortwave Broadcast Band Aerials	£1.95
BP133	An Introduction to Programming the Dragon 32	£1.95
BP135	Secrets of the Commodore 64	£1.95
BP136	25 Simple Indoor and Window Aerials	£1.75
BP137	BASIC & FORTRAN in Parallel	£1.95
BP138	BASIC & FORTH in Parallel	£1.95
BP139	An Introduction to Programming the BBC Model B Micro	£1.95
BP140	Digital IC Equivalents & Pin Connections	£5.95
BP141	Linear IC Equivalents & Pin Connections	£5.95
BP142	An Introduction to Programming the Acorn Electron	£1.95
BP143	An Introduction to Programming the Atari 600/800XL	£1.95
BP144	Further Practical Electronics Calculations and Formulae	£4.95
BP145	25 Simple Tropical and MW Band Aerials	£1.75
BP146	The Pre-BASIC Book	£2.95
BP147	An Introduction to 6502 Machine Code	£2.50
BP148	Computer Terminology Explained	£1.95
BP149	A Concise Introduction to the Language of BBC BASIC	£1.95
BP152	An Introduction to Z80 Machine Code	£2.75
BP153	An Introduction to Programming the Amstrad CPC464 and 664	£2.50
BP154	An Introduction to MSX BASIC	£2.50
BP156	An Introduction to QL Machine Code	£2.50
BP157	How to Write ZX Spectrum and Spectrum+ Games Programs	£2.50
BP158	An Introduction to Programming the Commodore 16 and Plus 4	£2.50
BP159	How to write Amstrad CPC 464 Games Programs	£2.50
BP161	Into the QL Archive	£2.50
BP162	Counting on QL Abacus	£2.50
BP169	How to Get Your Computer Programs Running	£2.50
BP170	An Introduction to Computer Peripherals	£2.50
BP171	Easy Add-on Projects for Amstrad CPC 464, 664, 6128 and MSX Computers	£3.50
BP173	Computer Music Projects	£2.95
BP174	More Advanced Electronic Music Projects	£2.95
BP175	How to Write Word Game Programs for the Amstrad CPC 464, 664 and 6128	£2.95
BP176	A TV-DXers Handbook	£5.95
BP177	An Introduction to Computer Communications	£2.95
BP179	Electronic Circuits for the Computer Control of Robots	£2.95
BP180	Electronic Circuits for the Computer Control of Model Railways	£2.95
BP181	Getting the Most from Your Printer	£2.95
BP182	MIDI Projects	£2.95
BP183	An Introduction to CP/M	£2.95
BP184	An Introduction to 68000 Assembly Language	£2.95
BP185	Electronic Synthesiser Construction	£2.95
BP186	Walkie-Talkie Projects	£2.95
BP187	A Practical Reference Guide to Word Processing on the Amstrad PCW8256 & PCW8512	£5.95
BP188	Getting Started with BASIC and LOGO on the Amstrad PCWs	£5.95
BP189	Using Your Amstrad CPC Disc Drives	£2.95
BP190	More Advanced Electronic Security Projects	£2.95
BP191	Simple Applications of the Amstrad CPCs for Writers	£2.95
BP192	More Advanced Power Supply Projects	£2.95
BP193	LOGO for Beginners	£2.95
BP194	Modern Opto Device Projects	£2.95
BP195	An Introduction to Satellite Television	£5.95
BP196	BASIC & LOGO in Parallel	£2.95
BP197	An Introduction to the Amstrad PC's	£5.95
BP198	An Introduction to Antenna Theory	£2.95
BP199	An Introduction to BASIC-2 on the Amstrad PC's	£5.95
BP230	An Introduction to GEM	£5.95
BP232	A Concise Introduction to MS-DOS	£2.95
BP233	Electronic Hobbyists Handbook	£4.95
BP234	Transistor Selector Guide	£4.95
BP235	Power Selector Guide	£4.95
BP236	Digital IC Selector Guide-Part 1	£4.95
BP237	Digital IC Selector Guide-Part 2	£4.95
BP238	Linear IC Selector Guide	£4.95
BP239	Getting the Most from Your Multimeter	£2.95
BP240	Remote Control Handbook	£3.95
BP241	An Introduction to 8086 Machine Code	£5.95
BP242	An Introduction to Computer Aided Drawing	£2.95
BP243	BBC BASIC86 on the Amstrad PC's and IBM Compatibles — Book 1: Language	£3.95
BP244	BBC BASIC86 on the Amstrad PC's and IBM Compatibles — Book 2: Graphics & Disc Files	£3.95
BP245	Digital Audio Projects	£2.95
BP246	Musical Applications of the Atari ST's	£4.95
BP247	More Advanced MIDI Projects	£2.95
BP248	Test Equipment Construction	£2.95
BP249	More Advanced Test Equipment Construction	£2.95
BP250	Programming in FORTRAN 77	£4.95
BP251	Computer Hobbyists Handbook	£5.95
BP252	An Introduction to C	£2.95
BP253	Ultra High Power Amplifier Construction	£3.95
BP254	From Atoms to Amperes	£2.95
BP255	International Radio Stations Guide	£4.95
BP256	An Introduction to Loudspeakers and Enclosure Design	£2.95
BP257	An Introduction to Amateur Radio	£2.95
BP258	Learning to Program in C	£4.95